RUNNING WITH THE DOLPHINS
AND OTHER TYBEE TALES

Dedicated to
Willie Adolphis Berry and Guy Gains Sayles, Jr.
two forty-year-olds playing pirates
(with apologies to Jimmy Buffett)

RUNNING WITH THE DOLPHINS
AND OTHER TYBEE TALES

Micheal Elliott

SMYTH & HELWYS
PUBLISHING. INC.

Macon, Georgia

ISBN 1-57312-006-5
Running with the Dolphins and Other Tybee Tales
Micheal Elliott

Copyright © 1995
Smyth & Helwys Publishing, Inc.
6316 Peake Road
Macon, Georgia 31210-3960
1-800-747-3016

Library of Congress Cataloging-in-Publication Data

Elliott, Micheal
    Running with the dolphins and other Tybee tales/Micheal Elliott.
    152+ viii pp.   6" x 9" (16 x 23 cm.)
    ISBN 1-57312-006-5 (acid-free paper)
    1. Tybee Island (Ga. : Island)—Social life and customs—Fiction.
    I. Title.
    PS3555.L592R86   1995
    813'.54—dc20

                                                        95-5840
                                                        CIP

Contents

"Some island with the sea's silence upon it…"
Robert Browning
Pippa Passes, Part II

Preface

S ince 1979 I have lived and worked with homeless people. During these years, I wrote four books, each dealing with my vocation. The first, *The Society of Salty Saints*, was the story of a congregation of which I was the pastor in the inner city of Louisville, Kentucky. After leaving that church, I continued to work with homeless people in my hometown of Savannah, Georgia. My writing reflected this experience, typically from a spiritual interpretation. In 1993 I wrote *Why the Homeless Don't Have Homes and What to Do about It*, which contained the majority of what I had to say about homelessness as a social and religious problem. The Midwest Book Achievement Awards recognized this book as the best paperback of the year, leaving me feeling that I had accomplished what I intended.

When I returned to Savannah, my family and I determined to live on Tybee, a small barrier island just to the south of Hilton Head, South Carolina. I had visited Tybee throughout my life and had always wanted to call it home. Each day I ride into Savannah where I continue to work with homeless people, those struggling to recover from substance abuse, and persons living with AIDS. It is an intense, and often public, life. At the end of the work day, my car sails across the causeway connecting Tybee to the mainland. After crossing the Bull River bridge, I can almost swear that a big door closes, shutting out that portion of my life. On Tybee, I am in another world. I am a homebody once on the island, preferring to work in the yard, hang out at The Breakfast Club, take walks with my wife, or sit on the beach. I grow resentful when something intrudes upon these goals. It is a reflective and slow-paced life. It is also the best of two worlds.

Having nothing else to say about my homeless friends, I began writing the stories I was fond of telling and the reflections of life on the island. More residential than most, Tybee is an island unlike others on the Georgia coast. Take away the ocean, and it is another small American town. Because of the sea, however, it attracts people who want to escape the real world. Tybee is "Mayberry on acid," as one friend describes it. Being called to work with homeless people is one thing, but having a life goal of being a beach bum is something entirely different. In some schizophrenic way, I try to balance both. The opportunity to come home and actually run with the dolphins brings this sense of balance to my life.

The stories here are as true as my memory allows them to be. Most of the characters encountered are neighbors. The names of persons have been changed to protect them from unwanted examination. In a few instances, composite characters represent several folks in one, so the story is told more efficiently. I have tried to capture what it feels like to live on Tybee, so those who visit can know what it is like to remain, and so that those of us fortunate enough to live here may remember what it is like now.

Susan Watts and Leslie Quarterman read the initial drafts and proved that a writer needs help with grammar. The good folks at Smyth & Helwys Publishing, Inc. forged a manuscript into a book. A few people who are not mentioned in the book merit a special expression of thanks. George and Ann Jacobs are dear friends who set the tone for celebrating life here. John and Jeannie Hutton, Daniel, Carolyn Sheehan and Eamon (who is lost in life while heading towards Notre Dame), Bobby and Sheila Phillips, George and George of the fabulous North Beach Grill, Curtis and Dee Carver, Wanda Kendrix, and the faculty of Saint Michael's school all contribute to making a neighborhood into a community. Janice, Jeremy, Kristen, and Chelsea comprise the perfect beach family and make a house into a home. God, the author of all oceanfront property, doesn't seem to be making as many beaches as in the past, and this makes me especially mindful of celebrating the island gifts that we do not have.

Tybee Then and Now

A s a native of Savannah, I was raised to have a special love for Tybee. There are prettier beaches, some even nearby, south of Jacksonville and north of Daytona Beach, Florida. The ocean water in the Gulf Stream far outshines the marsh-influenced sea off the coast of Georgia. Many island communities on the east coast are more attractive than the tiny town here. Yet, something is special about Tybee.

Like most people who live on the country's edge, the residents are eclectic and diverse. The municipality is like a thousand other small towns across the United States. Like reruns of Mayberry, it is a place that time and developers seem to have passed by. The smell of salt air in the breeze is familiar to

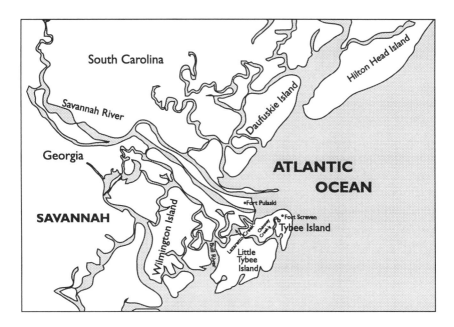

hundreds of thousands of people across the world. All of these characteristics of Tybee are common elements found elsewhere, but somehow Tybee is different. It is more than the sum of its parts.

What is this difference? How did it develop into the place it has become? Why are persons who are raised near it infected with its memory? What is it about this tiny, insignificant place that captivates the imagination of its older, historically important sister?

It all begins in the ocean. Eighty miles offshore the Gulf Stream flows out of the dark, deep water, bringing tropical warmth past the Georgia coast. The Gulf Stream water remains warm and tropical year-round and is filled with the life of the sea. Coral and sea weed, fish and mammals, bright colors and dark shapes are easily viewed through the clear sparkling water. This far out, there is no view of land, buoys, markers, or much of anything else. One will not likely see another boat or even a plane over the vast ocean. One can stand on the bow of a boat when the ocean is calm, listen to the continuance of quiet, observe the measureless sea and sky, and feel small and humble.

Mountain tops still offer firm support to those who dare to climb and peer a thousand feet into a canyon. Skyscrapers invoke feelings of admiration for the accomplishments of humanity. Few places on land can foster the deep feelings of standing in a tiny boat miles from shore and knowing that the water dominates everything. The vastness of the ocean coupled with the enormous amount of life makes a person feel part of the world in a way that he or she can rarely comprehend while surrounded by others. The Gulf Stream reminds us that life began here without the help of a single person.

The ocean floor erupts upward, and the bottom becomes flat and sandy, gradually ascending eastward until the waves lap against the shoreline. Appearing to be a desert under water, the water is not as clear, as it turns to a greenish-brown color. Still filled with life, it is not as crowded at Tybee as in the Gulf Stream. Dolphins swim in schools, breaking the surface in a smiling rhythm. Sand dollars bury themselves in bunches below the brownish-green sand. Stingrays swim in the choreographed V-shaped pattern commonly seen when seagulls fly overhead. Channel markers, buoys, and other signs of humanity begin to appear on the surface with increasing regularity as the water grows more shallow and ultimately ceases its flow.

A small strip of sand littered with shells, not yet completely broken into sand, continues the ascent until the mountains of dunes stand to protect the island. The dunes are covered with sea oats, morning glories, and other vegetation. To stand on top of a sand dune and gaze toward the sea is to understand what the Creation must have been like. Brownish-grey water laps against brownish-grey sand. Green marshes spread out behind the small island, two-and-a-half miles long and two-thirds of a mile wide.

The ocean can be seen from three sides of the island. From the back of the island is the broad Savannah River that separates it from Wilmington, an island covered with commerce and subdivisions. Standing in the dunes offers one the opportunity to observe the continuation of pure creation as the waves alter the shore and the dunes accumulate more sand. Everyday the beach is different, though most persons do not pause to consider the changes. It is rarely the same as the wind, and the water molds and shapes it.

Behind the beach is the island. In the early days of creation, beside the dunes ran a swamp. John Hutton describes the island's appearance in his marvelous book *Guale*.

> On [the] left was the ocean, which came up to a beach of what looked like mud and clay. The place looked like an old river bed that had dried up and had been taken over by bogs and marsh grasses. On [the] right, the swamp disappeared into a dense tangle of undergrowth. In front . . . a small path twisted through the swamp on narrow hummocks of grass.[1]

First inhabited by the Euclee Indians, the island was named Tybee, meaning salt. The name was accepted when the white men came, although no one cared to know what it meant for many years. Tybee was merely acknowledged as a part of the Spanish discovery of Florida. As Margaret Godley recorded,

> Before the *Susan Constant* sailed for Jamestown and before the Pilgrims landed on Plymouth Rock, Tybee Island had become known in history, as part of the Spanish claims in the New World . . . [as] part of the territory . . . called "La Florida." Also referred to as Bimini and later as Guale, this South Atlantic coastal territory extended from St. Augustine, Florida, northward to Port Royal, South Carolina.[2]

Known to the Spanish as "Los Bajos," Captain Francisco de Ecija described the island in the report of the first known naval battle on the Savannah River.

> The Bay of Los Bajos is a deep bay . . . it is a very wide harbor. . . . A fresh water river empties into it, and the channel of the bar is on the

south side close to a wooded point, below which there is another point, sandy. Within the bay, there is an island.[3]

When General James Oglethorpe founded the colony of Georgia, however, Tybee was used primarily as a military outpost. Lighthouses were built to steer ships safely into the Savannah harbor. When slavery came, Tybee played the role of the quarantine for Africans until they were deemed well enough to be sold. Lazaretto, now the name of the creek separating the island from the back marsh, means "hospital" in Spanish and was the name of the slave site. To walk this area is to hear the ghosts of people still crying for another beach on the other side of the ocean. The skulls of the sick are sometimes uncovered in a dark, eerie marsh, with black mud sending a shutter up the spine of those who care to walk here.

During the Civil War, Tybee quickly fell into northern hands and was the base for the attack on Fort Plusaki. "You might as well bombard the Rocky Mountains," said General Joseph G. Totten, chief engineer of the United States Army, when describing the newly constructed fort.[4] Ultimately, the northern army based its guns, including a newly developed one, on the north end of the Island.

Godley described the attack:

When the bombardment began, Pulaski guns replied vigorously to the batteries at Tybee. Within a few hours . . . the guns powerful enough to strike the fort were opening a breach through the walls, illustrating for the first time in actual warfare the breaching power of rifled guns at long range. One by one, the guns facing Tybee had been disabled, and firing in this direction was continued during the night to keep the Confederates from repairing the damage. By noon of the second day, the shells fired from Tybee were passing through an opening on the southeastern side of the fort and reaching the powder magazine. The walls were crumbling under heavy bombardment, and at 2 o'clock, observers on Tybee Island saw the Confederate colors flutter at half-mast and go slowly down.[5]

The fort, believed to be strong enough to withstand any attack, was quickly penetrated. The Confederate troops, under the command of General Olmstead, surrendered. The signs of the attack are still visible on the north wall of the fort.

After the war, the island was inhabited by a small but loyal community that fought against nature to survive. When the ocean displayed its wrath, and hurricanes slammed against the island, fathers would tie their children to trees so that, while the sand might blow away, the family would not. There are vivid descriptions of such episodes in the Tybee library, where guests may spend several hours learning what island life was like before The Weather Channel. In those days, hurricanes simply happened, and residents had little warning. Several times the entire island bore the brunt of such storms.

In the early days of the twentieth century, a railroad was built to connect the island with Savannah, and a popular resort was established. A pier was constructed that hosted the big bands of the era. Fort Screven, a military outpost, anchored the community. The municipality surrounding the fort was a bedroom community that owed its existence to the military. During this time, islanders worked for either the fort for the city, or they lived off the bounty of the ocean.

Old-timers gleefully reminisce about these days. Butler Avenue, the island's main thoroughfare, was a simple shell covered road lined with palm trees. Children were transported by wagon to school each morning. On Saturday nights, couples danced on the pier to the sounds of Benny Goodman and Duke Ellington. On weekends, islanders would work as hosts to the hundreds who rode the train from Savannah.

The fort closed in the 1940s, and the pier burned in the 1960s, followed by the destruction of several of the old grand hotels. Few remnants of Tybee's past remain. Pieces of Fort Screven lay scattered on the north end of the island like a child's discarded toys. The lighthouse, rebuilt several times, stands proud, and continues to offer its beacon to the ships of the sea. The seawall, built by the WPA of the Great Depression, still stands, more or less, protecting the island from the ocean. Visiting Tybee is acknowledging that the ocean is the only attraction left.

Most people love the ocean and have their favorite seaside spots for rest and relaxation. New Yorkers travel the train to Rockaway to escape from the city. Residents of Washington, D.C. drive two hours and retreat to the coast of Virginia. Each summer people in Wilmington, North Carolina migrate to Myrtle Beach, South Carolina, the shag capital of the world, where millions of baby boomers bop in the sand. Florida and California are meccas of sunshine and ultraviolet rays; their beaches draw millions of people each year. Thousands of oceanside communities serve as the special destination of millions of people, with each one referred to as a little piece of heaven.

Love of Tybee is more localized than other seaside communities. If most people have a romanticized love of these places, the city of Savannah has an obsession for Tybee Island. Many city residents have summer homes on the island, a fact easily reflected in the year-round Tybee population of approximately 3,000 families as compared to the summer throngs of over 10,000.

Most of the summer homes are old beach houses built in the 1930s and reflect the middle and upper crust of Savannah society. Many of the houses still have tiny servants quarters downstairs and large spacious rooms upstairs. Relics of a time gone by, these houses are testimony to the time before the beach was integrated. Current owners will reminisce about the old days when the "help" did all of the cooking and cleaning so the family could really enjoy the beach without having to worry about wet and sandy towels or having to cook supper after spending a day in the sun. Of course, the "help" stayed inside doing the washing and preparing the meals.

Savannah's upper crust has been labeled as quite clickish by outsiders, as is evident in their views of Tybee. Viewing the island as their own private summer retreat, they abhor any change the city of Tybee may propose. Because so many Tybee homeowners are, in fact, influential residents of Savannah, for years they have attempted to influence the island to develop as they desired. Permanent citizens of the island have been viewed as simple island people to be enjoyed in the same way as the scenery or the ocean. During the 1960s, Savannahians used their influence to have the name of the island changed to Savannah Beach! Citizens of Tybee refused to recognize this desecration and fought until the proper name was restored.

Persons choosing to make Tybee their permanent home embodied an individualism that John Wayne would envy and Savannah's visionaries would loathe. Given the choice between the ocean and high-rise apartment complexes, shopping malls and even hospitals, islanders claimed the sea was enough. Sometimes Tybee went too far exerting its independence and ended up keeping the island stuck in the 1950s. In the end, however, this has proven to not be all bad. While other islands are overrun by condominiums, malls, and emergency medical clinics, Tybee seems to remain frozen in time.

In the 1980s, people began to "discover" Tybee and relocate from other parts of the country to make the tiny island their permanent home. Consequently, the leadership of the Tybee government has experienced significant changes, and the domination of Savannah influences—while still great—has diminished.

Tybee: Then and Now

Although permanent residents may work "downtown" and make the daily commute to Savannah, they claim to have "Tybee-itis," a sense of dread when crossing the Lazaretto Creek bridge. Their love for Tybee is often expressed by disdain for Savannah. "Let's blow up the bridge!" is a common rallying cry. "We don't need a mall!" In fact, people who go to the mall are often ridiculed by those with a severe case of Tybee-itis.

Savannah has beautiful squares, cobblestone streets, restored historic homes and inns, and the same problems as other American cities. Crime, homelessness, drugs, and poverty are the primary concerns of city folks. On the island, the environment and small town gossip are the principal considerations. While Earth Day is ignored in Savannah, marsh walks celebrate the event on Tybee. Some people even claim that every day is Earth Day on the island.

The influence of nature is strong for islanders. They are close to the sand and soil. Many residents are staunch environmentalists, working hard to clean up the debris left by visitors. Beach sweeps are organized on a regular basis, where locals fill huge garbage bags with everything from beer cans to items of clothing. Visitors from Savannah are most often blamed for the untidiness. Islanders also participate in dolphin watch projects in order to learn more about the creatures with which they share the sea. Savannah merely names roads after dolphins and other creatures from the sea.

In spite of a love/hate relationship with Savannah, residents are proud of Tybee and enjoy hosting visitors. They demand respect for the island and ocean, however, and are quick to address flagrant insolence for the beauty of nature from visitors. These people recognize what a privilege it is to call Tybee home and view the island as a gift that should be held in high esteem. To live on Tybee is to have an appreciation for the beauty of nature that few others have. When the Euclee Indians named the island Tybee, which means salt, they were describing the numerous salt water creeks flowing in from the ocean. Hundreds of years later, we may also construe that they were characterizing the people.

Unlike Hilton Head to the north, and Jekyll to the south, the people of Tybee never learned that the sea is synonymous with golf courses. While other islands boast of eighteen holes, each with a view of the water, the only holes on Tybee are the ones in the road. Tourists seem to be blue collar sorts, working Monday through Friday and begging for overtime and a good deal on a one-week vacation that won't allow them to fall further into debt.

Tybee offers cheap hotel rooms, the best tourist attractions of the 1940s, and the ocean. There are no theme parks worthy of Disney, although an amusement park with a merry-go-round is open during the summer months. Overpriced restaurants with panoramic views of the ocean are missing; but Christy's serves good corn dogs, the Marina steams oysters on Saturdays, the Hunter House has fine food served in an intimate atmosphere, MacElwees has the best seafood platter, and George and George (on the north end) makes the best crab cake sandwiches around.

The closest thing Tybee has to an aquarium is whatever washes up on the beach. The hotels are not elaborate but provide a night's sleep between days spent beside the surf or fishing trips. For the most part, few things compel people to visit—except the sea.

Living here is what it must be like if the mythical Mayberry and Andy and Barney had been located at the beach. City Hall is small and sits in the middle of the island. The police department employs a force that mostly gives speeding tickets, breaks up fights, and drives inebriated locals home after a good time on the town.

There are several convenience stores, one gas station, a grocery store, and a post office that does not deliver. The Tybee newspaper comes out monthly but makes little sense unless one lives here. The public school is not located on the island, meaning that most students must ride the bus for half-an-hour one way.

The year-round population is small enough so that most everyone has occasion to run into most everyone else at the post office or grocery store. Residents place a sticker on the back of their cars that give them the right to park anywhere they please for free, while visitors must pay one quarter for every hour.

From September through May the island is laid back and quiet. Residents may take long walks on the beach and rarely pass a neighbor. The winters consist mostly of a cold windy season that lasts from January through March. People swim in the surf well into November and as early as March. Residents enjoy this time of year most. There are few tourists, little traffic, and few reasons to interrupt one's solitude. The off-season is a time for reflection and contemplation, when the windows are left open to allow the constant sea breeze to blow salt air through the house and the outside to come home. The quiet is only interrupted by the constant sound of the waves and water.

Tybee: Then and Now

The summer months are filled with noisy commotion. Restaurants are full. The beach is crowded and littered. Traffic is constant and loud. Windows are closed, and air conditioners are turned on, as much to keep the noise out as the coolness in. Those souls who are brave enough to venture outside are immediately confronted with soda pop and beer cans discarded in their yards, vehicles turning around in their driveways, and inquiries about parking on one's property.

Walking down the beach is to see thousands of cigarette butts washed along the shoreline; trip over broken chairs left by long-gone owners; and risk physical assault from flying frisbees, tennis balls, baseballs, or velcro spheres that take the skin off one's forehead when they hit. Summer is one long circus residents watch that requires no tickets. Those who love to people-watch are never bored; those seeking the solitude of the sea buy a boat.

If it appears that citizens of Tybee disdain summer, they do and they don't. Most of them enjoy watching people enjoy the ocean, children playing in the waves, families lunching on the beach, and lovers strolling in the surf. It is quite another thing to discover soiled diapers in the middle of the road or listen to teenagers cuss like sailors in front of one's own children or drive cars down a dead-end street at a thousand miles per hour with radios blaring.

For the most part, Tybee residents take the circus in stride. They appreciate the revenue tourists generate, take advantage of a good time when they see one, and know that in September the beach will be quiet again. Nowhere is this knowledge more pronounced than at the annual Beach Bum Celebration.

On the weekend before Memorial Day, the residents of Tybee stage their own parade, a celebration of the ocean before the tourist season begins. Residents dress up in their tackiest tourist garb, climb into cars or onto floats sponsored by area businesses, and follow the procession down Butler Avenue. The Beach Bum steering committee chooses a king and queen, who ride in honor at the front of the parade.

Those residents who do not actually participate in the parade hook up their garden hoses and take their seats in folding lawn chairs that line the route. As the procession passes, people in the parade throw water balloons at people watching who, in turn, throw balloons back or shoot water from their hoses. It is one long, wet, fun affair. The last entry in the parade is the fire engine shooting its massive hose at everyone watching. The only persons

9

who do not get wet are those who do not attend. Water sports take on a new meaning at Tybee.

This practice may sound offensive to someone who attends unaware. A few years ago the chairman of the county commission arrived for the parade dressed in a business suit and prepared to thank his constituents for electing him to office. The first mile of the parade proved to be safe enough, although water balloons did fly perilously close to his head. Eventually the inevitable happened.

A few residents impersonating tourists leaped in front of the chairman's convertible, water balloons raised in hand. The chairman's grin quickly turned to horror as he realized that they had every intention of throwing them at close range. Before his protest could be heard above the roar of approval, three perfectly-thrown balloons hit his chest in rapid succession. When he stood to protest, other residents turned their hoses on him, baptizing the chairman in their appreciation. He was the last chairman of the county commission to actually ride in the parade, although others have chosen to watch from the yards of their friends' homes.

After the parade is over, residents retreat to their homes for private parties or venture to island bars for additional mayhem. The private parties are normally on docks or decks and center around barbeque. The bars host bands playing beach music as residents shag and drink beer. Afterwards, each resident has remembered what summer is like.

All of this activity is somehow a celebration of creation. Sitting beside the ocean, it is easy to imagine what the world must have been like when it was "void and covered with darkness." The water had yet to be separated from the land. Then in the first act of creation, it happened. People on Tybee live with one foot in the ocean and the other on the beach. The water is too murky to see all of the life that fills it. Fish, shells, sand dollars, jelly fish, dolphins, stingrays, crabs, and sharks swim with us.

To face the ocean with one's back to the community is to begin comprehending creation. From the smallest fish to the largest whale, human beings stand in awe of the things they did not create. Turning around we see the buildings, telephone poles, houses, and cars. Artificial lights over massive parking lots draw sea turtles from the ocean to lay hundreds of eggs in the sand on which we throw frisbees, to be trampled on by volleyball games and crowds of sun worshipers.

Tybee: Then and Now

The order of creation is disturbed by humanity's wishes, as with overdeveloped and exclusive islands, but the balance still swings in creation's favor on Tybee. John MacDonald described what we do to creation.

> There are miles of beach, and there are miles of bunnies along the tan Atlantic sand. When the public beach ended, I came to the great white wall of high-rise condominiums which conceal the sea and partition the sky. They are compartmented boxes stacked high in sterile sameness. The balconied ghetto. Soundproof by the sea. So many conveniences and security factors that life at last is reduced to ultimate boredom, to the great decisions of the day—which channel to watch and whether to swim in the sea or the pool.[6]

Tybee celebrates the fact that it is different. There are few condominiums, no tall buildings, and little to do except appreciate the beauty of the island and ocean with few distractions. A friend who lived here once commented, "Tybee today is what Key West was like in the 1970s before it turned into what Jimmy Buffett called a 'boutique'." Coming to Tybee is a step back in time, coming to a place that has struck a balance between creation and commerce. Everyday the people who live here and those who visit celebrate the balance.

God doesn't seem to be in the business of creating much more oceanfront property. Though developers think the sea is synonymous with high-rise ghettos, Tybee has been able to detour from such development, and the contractors are kept at bay. The celebration of creation continues for everyone, and the bums have their beach.

Notes

[1]John Hutton, *Guale* (Savannah GA: American Efficiency Publications, 1993) 53-54.

[2]Margaret Godley, *Historic Tybee Island* (Savannah Beach GA: The Tybee Museum Association, 1958) 1.

[3]Ibid., 3.

[4]Ibid., 19.

[5]Ibid., 31.

[6]John MacDonald, *A Tan and Shady Silence* (New York: Harper & Row, 1985) 28.

The Young Man and the Sea

On a rainy Saturday afternoon the family piled into the car and drove the twenty miles to Williams Seafood to feast on fried and broiled seafood. Afterwards we drove the additional ten miles to Tybee Island and parked in the big lot at the end of Sixteenth Street. My parents watched the warm summer rain fall into the ocean while my brother and I excitedly bounced around the back seat, dying to get out of the car. When they could no longer stand us, my father said we could run around if we wanted. Climbing over one another, we fell out of the car and hurried to the beach where we ran around like mad men in the rain.

Inching closer to the ocean, we reasoned there was no difference between getting wet by the rain or the sea. After all, wet is wet regardless of the cause. The waves were high and perfect for body surfing. Standing in waist-deep water, we waited for the waves to peak. At the moment when they began to roll over, we smoothly slid our bodies into the breaking wave, catching the roll and riding the crash into the shore. Quickly making a game out of it, we raced to see who could ride a wave the fastest and farthest. When close to the shore, we waved at our parents, who were still thankful for the peace that filled the car because of our absence.

Eventually, however, they called us in. Laughingly, we ran to the automobile and heard our mother complain that we were soaking wet and had no towels. My father said it was all right to use our shirts to dry off. The windows fogged in the car, which provoked us to draw on them with our fingers until we arrived home. Weary from the food, the swim, and the ride, we quickly fell asleep and left our parents with a temporary sense of peace and a very wet back seat.

Trips to Tybee were simply part of growing up in Savannah. We made regular jaunts with family and friends. Because my father could not afford many traveling vacations, we often spent several days on the convenient and cheap island, just as thousands of other working families did. Because it was close, had very affordable hotel rooms, and the entertainment of the ocean was free, Tybee offered a very reasonably-priced, yet exotic, respite. Because it has refrained from the development of high rise condominiums, the island still largely caters to middle class working families.

Later that summer we returned to Tybee and stayed several days with a friend who owned a cottage at the beach. Daily we packed a cooler with soft drinks and sandwiches and chose just the right spot near the sea. In the 1960s Tybee still had a massive pier and amusement park. Wandering around the pilings that held it above the water inspired a sense of awe and adventure. While my mother bathed herself in the sun, I wandered in the cool dampness under the pier.

Pretending to be James Bond, I hid behind pilings and gathered information on couples kissing in the darker shadows, shell collectors filling their bags, and fishermen who waded into the surf to cast their lines. The couples groping one another's lips were simply not interesting enough to hold my attention. And who in their right mind would collect broken shells? My attention focused on a fisherman. Darting from one piling to another, I secretly made my way closer to the waves breaking under the pier. My goal was the piling closest to the fisherman's bucket. I had observed that whenever he caught a fish, he tied it to a string fixed to the piling. It merited further investigation.

The fisherman baited his hook and turned to the sea. Wading out into the surf, he cast his line and kept a watchful eye on it. This was my chance. Ever so silently, I stole to the piling. Checking to make certain he was still fishing, I picked up the string of fish. It seemed as though the world stopped turning as I held what must have been a hundred different kinds of fish, some still flapping around in a vain attempt to shake the string that ran through their gills. I thought they were beautiful.

No longer wanting to play James Bond, I now wanted to be a fisherman with a catch like this one. Wouldn't my parents be proud if I came back from a day of fishing with this kind of bounty? My father could teach me how to clean them, and we could fry fish for supper. Why not? Without checking with the fisherman, I bolted out from under the pier carrying the string of fish. In the bright light, I proudly carried the catch to my parents. People who didn't know better watched with envy as I strutted with the line of fish. I knew it looked impressive. When I reached my mother, I displayed the treasure.

"Where did you get those?" she demanded. Something in the tone of her voice told me she was not pleased.

"Er . . . I found them under the pier," I explained, no longer confident in the treasures in my hand.

"Who caught those fish?"

Reverting back to James Bond, I wondered how a master spy would respond when caught red-handed. Should I shoot her and run? Should I explain how I caught them bare-handed? What was the most plausible story? My mind raced as I weighed my options.

"Somebody left them," was the best I could do.

"Well, take them back."

Take them back? I was horrified. How could my mother not appreciate the beauty of such a fine catch?

"Right this very instant!" she commanded.

I slowly turned and made my way to the pier. The catch no longer seemed as large or as exciting as it had been a few moments earlier. In fact, the fish felt heavy. Again I entered the cool dampness under the pier. Stealing from piling to piling, I made my way back to the fisherman. He was still in the surf watching his line and waiting on the next strike.

I tied the string and retreated to the darkness where the couples were, cursing my mother's lack of appreciation. There was no reason to feel bad for the fisherman, I reasoned, because he would catch more. The adventure was over, and the mission had lost its luster. I returned to my rather stupid family, where my mother promptly spanked me and cautioned me to never steal again.

When I finished crying, she told me to go swimming and have a good time. Walking towards the water, I wished I could go home. The soothing sound of the waves must have calmed me, because ten minutes later—or perhaps it was because I was only ten—I was again frolicking in the ocean, having the time of my life, wishing I could stay at Tybee forever.

Later that week, on the last night of our stay, we returned to the pier. After a supper of corn dogs, french fries, and cotton candy, we strolled to the amusement park. Loud music blasted from a juke box that was surrounded by a crowd of teenagers wearing swimsuits. They danced to the "Wooly Booly" sounds of Sam the Sham and the Pharaohs.

One girl, wearing a string bikini, wildly moved around the dance floor. My father commented to his friend that if he ever had a daughter, she would never be allowed to do anything like that. Looking at the girl, I suddenly thought she was the most beautiful thing I had ever seen. Although it would not blossom for several more years, a new reason to enjoy the beach was planting its seed in my mind.

We continued walking on the pier when my father suggested we go to the shooting gallery. A small, white frame, firing range—only ten or fifteen feet wide and what seemed like two miles deep—stood between a shell shop and an ice cream stand. After paying twenty-five cents for ten shots, I picked up a rifle and took aim at the ducks and cards rolling on a conveyer belt at the far end of the gallery. I actually hit several of the ducks and heard a loud *PING* of the pellet as it bounced off the metal duck and knocked it down. That adventure was as much fun as watching the girl in the bikini. All too soon my father said it was time to move on.

Entering the amusement park that was situated near the pier, we purchased tickets for the ferris wheel. We had visited larger and more elaborate wheels, but Tybee's appeared to be the fastest. It spun around at neck-breaking speed, forcing one's stomach into his or her throat with each revolution. Most riders were not aware of the speed as they gleefully climbed aboard, but as it started spinning, children suddenly screamed, "Let me off! Let me off!" The wheel operators—with shoulder-length hair, tatoos on their arms, and ears that obviously did not work—continued to allow the wheel to pick up speed.

All riders quickly reached the conclusion that the wheel would snap at any second and everyone would roll into the ocean. Most of them struck bargains with God and mentally listed personal wills. As the wheel was spinning around, the entire island became a blur, and I tried to figure out which way to lean when I threw up. At just that moment, the wheel slowed to a normal speed and then stopped. The car I was in sat at the very pinnacle of the wheel. Looking down, I saw people on rubbery knees joyfully exiting the wheel.

When my eyes turned upward, they beheld one of the most beautiful sights in the world. A panoramic view of the ocean spread out before me. To the left was the lighthouse throwing its beacon in every direction. Street lights appeared as stationary fire flies lined up in single file and standing at attention. The rooftops of houses surrounded us in dark contrast to the blinking colors of the amusement park. It was the ocean that demanded attention, however, as a full moon cast its own soft light on the water, leaving a trail of brightness that looked like a sidewalk had been built on the sea.

The Young Man and the Sea

My father said how pretty it was and then began to rock the car in which we were sitting.

I already had enough motion for one night and felt the fear of falling overwhelm me again. I asked him to stop, but he continued shifting his weight from one side of the car to the other, laughing and asking me if I wanted to land upside down. "Stop!" I screamed. "Stop!" The ferris wheel must affect one's hearing because, like the men who operate it, my father didn't seem to hear me.

As he continued rocking, I kept my eyes fixed on the ocean. Sitting on top of the world, looking down at the sea, I was filled with an appreciation of the beauty of creation for the first time in my young life. I thought the world must look like that when it is viewed from heaven. All too soon the wheel resumed its spinning, and I again wondered which way to lean. Mercifully, it stopped before it made a full revolution. The metal bar that held us in was disconnected by the long-haired, tattooed attendant; and we, too, walked away on rubbery knees.

Strolling beside the beach, I again viewed the trail of light on the water, this time at ground level. It was just as beautiful as the view from heaven. Walking to the beach house, the moon's trail seemed to follow us as though inviting the family to take a walk on the water. The sound of the waves hugging the shore filled the night air. I lagged behind my family, staring at the water's light and wishing I could walk out there.

Family visits to Tybee continued for us as the years passed, and we continued to rent hotel rooms or stay with friends. Although we took vacations to the North Carolina mountains or beaches of Daytona, like many Savannahians, we spent most family holidays on the island closest to us. As I grew older, I soon discovered a new appreciation for going to Tybee. The seed planted beside the bikini-clad dancer was growing too.

Beach Talk

I have spent thousands of hours watching girls and women walk Tybee's beach, sunbathe in the sun, or frolick in the ocean. If anything can compare with the beauty of the sea, it is the creatures who flock to its shore on any given day.

Upon reaching sixteen years of age, I obtained my driver's license and began making regular trips to Tybee without my family. Parking at Fort Screven or in the Sixteenth Street lot, I would take off my shirt, flex whatever muscles I may or may not have had, and stroll down the beach. This activity was called "land trolling" and is very similar to what fishermen do when they set their lines off the boat and drag them along waiting for big fish to strike. Land trolling is an art known to every generation of teenagers who has ever visited the beach, and it can occur in several ways.

First, after flexing muscles or making certain the bathing suit is adjusted just right, you walk down the beach until you pass someone you wish to impress. The walk is then slowed so that the object of desire is afforded every opportunity to at least notice your existence. Once you are confident that person has noticed, eye contact can be made, a smile may be flashed, and words might be spoken. Now that the bait has been cast, you may either continue to walk or stop and strike up a conversation. "Sure is a pretty day," you might say. "Uh-huh," he or she may answer. The bait is either swallowed whole, and a real conversation takes place; or it simply rots in the sun, and the smell of the soured attempt forces you to walk away briskly.

A second method of land trolling is to find someone else who is trolling, preferably of the opposite sex, and follow the person. Eventually the gap is closed, and the two trollers fall into step with each other. As a sixteen-year-old, this was my personal favorite as it allowed the opportunity for the other person to speak first. "Do you want something?" she might ask. "Sure is a pretty day," I would answer, stopping in my tracks as she continued walking.

A third method is only employed by the boldest of trollers. My best friend Jerry was such a person. Upon arriving at the beach and removing his shirt, he would grab a bottle of suntan lotion. Choosing the closest object of his desire, he would walk straight up to her, explain that he was alone, and politely ask if she would mind helping him to apply the lotion to his hard-to-reach back. I was always amazed that his method worked more often than not, and Jerry would wink at me as he sat down next to his newest best friend, leaving me to troll by myself.

I tried Jerry's method once or twice, after much prodding from the expert, but always seemed to choose girls who had boyfriends I had not spotted. When this happened, I would fall back on the only recourse I had in confronting the situation. "Sure is a nice day," I would explain as I walked away.

Regardless of the method of trolling, I would typically end up taking long solitary walks, staring out to sea and lost in thought. Most often, I wished a female land troller would fall into step beside me or a mermaid would ride a wave to my feet. It never happened of course, but I still have a tremendous amount of sympathy for the sailors who confused manatees with mermaids in the last century.

On numerous occasions I would sit by the water's edge, turn my back on the thousands of trollers, and contemplate the ocean. I wondered about life under the sea. In the same water in which my feet were cooling were great whales, terrible sharks, and colorful fish. I felt a part of the larger sense of creation somehow.

Those periods of contemplation are what I recall most about my adolescence. Girls occupied my mind from time to time, but when I was at Tybee I brooded about the larger world. Though I did not know the word "theophany" (God expressing divinity through nature) at the time, I somehow knew the meaning. The ancient people believed that if a massive dark storm appeared, God was expressing anger; and if an eclipse occurred, God was absent from humanity. I do not remember those dark expressions; rather, I recall some very positive statement that was both overwhelming and affirming.

Having grown up in the same part of the country as author Pat Conroy, I remembered the feelings of a sixteen-year-old when I read these words:

> The sun, red and enormous, began to sink in the western sky and simultaneously the moon began to rise on the other side of the river with its own glorious shade of red, coming up out of the trees like a russet fire

bird. The sun and the moon seemed to acknowledge each other and they moved in both apposition and concordance in a breathtaking dance of light across the oaks and the palms. My father watched it and I thought he would cry again. He had returned to the sea . . . and his heart was a low country heart. The children were screaming, pointing to the sun, then turning to look at the rising moon, calling to the sun, then to the moon.[1]

Sitting alone on the beach during the formative years is stimulation to view life and creation in their broadest terms. Perhaps it is because of the expanse of the ocean. The air may be cleaner and the sky clearer. Sea and sun and moon all seem to complement each other in ways that do not occur with as much regularity elsewhere. The sound of the sea—waves crashing on the shore, gulls flying overhead, pelicans diving in the water—led me to believe that nature talks back when you stop to listen.

In the mountains or in a field, you have a sense of viewing nature as though you were in a museum, quietly reflecting on the scenery and inter-rupted by the occasional rustling of the wind. At the ocean the sounds of creation are all around, the salt air fills your lungs, and the beckoning waves fill your ears. When Moses stood before the burning bush, he took his shoes off in honor of the holiness of the sight. I have noticed that few people wear shoes at the beach, obviously in appreciation of the same fact.

Once I sat beside the water's edge observing a thundershower several miles offshore. As lightening flashed in the distance and rain poured from the dark foreboding clouds, the bright sun bathed me in warmth on the beach. It seemed as though any problems I may have had were "out there." At the beach, it always seems this way. I suppose the vastness of the sea makes one feel small and lost in the universe.

People who live near the ocean are fond of repeating this saying: "Once salt air gets in your veins you will always be drawn to the sea." I have come to believe this statement is utterly true. My earliest memories of Tybee are precious ones and represent the initial transfusions of salt air mixed with human blood. The hours I spent noticing the ocean were a primary catalyst in the development of my ways of thinking. Life seemed to have a proper balance so long as I looked to the sea. Often in life, however, we must leave something or some place in order to appreciate how much it means to us.

Note

[1] *Prince of Tides* (Boston: Houghton Mifflin, 1986) 566.

Land-Locked

After graduating from high school, I attended a college some sixty miles from the coast. College days were exciting and frightening. Many changes occurred in rapid succession during those years. The first year was a time to sow wilds oats, which I did with reckless abandon. During the second year, I met the woman who became my wife. During the third year we were married, and the following year our son was born. Finally, I crammed four years of college into five and determined I wanted to attend seminary.

Throughout those events, Tybee remained a constant in my life. I regularly made trips back to the island when I needed time alone. I courted my future wife there, and during warm spring days we would sun outside the dormitory until we could no longer stand it and impulsively make a decision to drive to the beach so that we could be wind burned. We also spent our honeymoon beside the ocean.

After college graduation, we moved to the land-locked area called Kentucky where we lived and worked for eight years so that I could attend seminary. Living in a land-locked country was a new and often frustrating experience. While we thought Kentucky, Ohio, Indiana, and other states had their own unique beauty, and the Ohio River was a beautiful site when viewed from a high, rock-covered bluff, something always seemed to be missing. I wondered how long it took the river water to travel to the ocean. I quickly discarded such thoughts, as there were so many new things to experience in my new home.

I learned that seafood in Kentucky is much different from the real thing. We sometimes visited a restaurant in Kentucky when we *had to have* seafood. After the waitress would recount the evening's specials, I would study the menu and often discover that white fish was available. "What is white fish?" I would ask. "Well," she would explain, "that would be fish that is white."

"But is it flounder, whiting, dolphin?" I would inquire. "It is a very good fish that is white. I can assure you that it is fresh."

I was not convinced, but ordered it anyway. Hoping it would be flounder, the fried substance that arrived on my plate was reminiscent of the finest fried leather available. When covered with a gallon of tarter sauce, it wasn't that bad, but when we left I wanted real seafood all the more.

We ended up trying it all. Long John Silver's provided the best fish batter around; unfortunately there was no fish on the plate. Captain D's served something that was cut in the shape of shrimp, but had no taste. Western Sizzler had a Friday night seafood buffet that served all-you-can-eat shrimp. We ordered and re-ordered gleefully, peeling away the fried batter and eating nothing more than the tiny molecules of shrimp meat at the center—until the waiter informed us this was an unacceptable way to eat seafood and he could no longer serve us.

Lucky for us, a fellow student from Gulf Shores, Alabama was experiencing the same problem. When he drove home on weekends, he would load his trunk with *real* seafood and return to the land-locked country. People began offering to purchase the unburied treasures from him, and the trips became more frequent. He soon purchased a large truck to accommodate larger loads and hired a second driver so the trips could occur more often. Still later he realized that God had not called him to seminary to save the lost from hell as much as to save the people of Louisville from bad seafood. Realizing he would make more money with his treasures from the sea, he withdrew from his classes and opened a fresh seafood shop, much to my delight and the joy of the rest of the famished masses.

Another significant factor in our ability to survive away from the ocean was the fact that the decade of the eighties was a most productive time in the musical career of Jimmy Buffet. I quickly cultivated an appreciation for the creole sounds of a steel drum and was transformed into a "parrot-head" (the term Buffet uses to describe his fans).

One cold morning in February, I arrived at the campus for my eight o'clock class. Sitting in the car, trying to muster enough courage and warmth to make the dash through the snow flurries, I heard a familiar voice over the radio. He sang of leaving Cincinnati, only ninety miles from Louisville and just as cold, looking for peace and quiet, hoping to see the sun again. Looking through the windshield at the bitter wind causing the trees to bend, I was swept back to the top of Tybee.

Land-Locked

The view from the Tybee lighthouse at dusk filled my mind. Atop the tall black and white tower, the ocean was easily seen as the night began to engulf the waters. Ships from around the world were located at the mouth of the channel waiting for the tide to allow them to enter the port at Savannah. Faint stars in the sky hung above the bright lights on the ships that looked like stars on the water. From that vantage point, I could focus my gaze on the vague point where the ocean ends and the sky begins, where the flying stars and floating stars meet.

Behind me were the city lights of Savannah, some seventeen miles inland. Bringing my eyes toward those lights, Cockspur Island lay between Tybee and the mainland. To the right lay Daufuskie Island, a large green mass floating in the ocean. Completing the circle, my eyes again rested upon the sea. At such a high vantage point, the warm wind blew.

My mind regained the actual communication signal the eyes were sending. The wind was bitterly cold, and the trees were frozen. The song continued about keeping dreams afloat, rolling in the sand, and searching for peace and quiet. Though it was 1982, and it would actually take five more years, at that moment, 7:50 in the morning, I knew the course I wanted my life to take. Tybee was too much a part of who I was. The salt was in my veins, and visions of palm trees filled my mind. It was still cold, but I was warmed with ocean memories and dreamy songs.

That night, I bought the Jimmy Buffet album in a K-Mart and stayed up late listening to songs about the sea. Janice and I reminded each other of the times we had spent on Tybee and seriously began discussing the possibility of one day moving there. We were homesick, tired of the demands of a large city and sick of being cold. We promised ourselves that as soon as possible, we would go home to a place where we had never lived. It was as poignant a promise as any vow I had made in seminary.

We finally made the move, doing everything backwards. First we purchased the house. Janice flew to Savannah where she and my father toured Tybee until she found one. My mother lived in Savannah and kept a watch for houses we could afford. We planned to continue living in Louisville until we could obtain employment in Savannah, but knowing we owned a home on Tybee was too much.

Several weeks later in true beach-bum fashion, Janice and I, along with our children, reasoned that jobs would take care of themselves and packed our meager belongings into a friend's truck and hauled them to Georgia. The young man who grew up between the river and the sea was returning older and ready to experience the transformation from a fairly normal human being to a beach bum. In the coming years, I would have a lot of help from local experts.

The Weather God

In the fall of 1987, we moved into our first house on Tybee. Tenth Street is the center of the island and, I am told, the highest level of elevation—three feet. Of course, I have no idea how to measure sea level, so this information has little value to me. Is my house three feet higher than the sea at high tide or low tide? Is the mean level of the sea measured? What is the definition of "level of the sea"? My understanding is: I hope the sea doesn't get mean and level my house.

When we purchased the house, my friends in Louisville warned me about hurricanes. I suppose they all had lived through the horrible hurricanes on the Ohio River and wanted to save me from the experience. To live on an island, however, is to experience the threat of hurricanes in the fall of the year. Our first experience came with Hugo.

When a storm at sea begins to swirl in a circular motion, residents of the island take notice. They pay constant attention to wind speed and the general direction the storm appears to be heading. They begin praying to The Weather Channel, seeking to turn the storm a few degrees in either direction. The area McDonald's corporation has Ronald distributing free hurricane tracking maps so children can follow the storm from its point of origin all the way to their house.

Television weather reporters get even more time on the air to explain the history of hurricanes, review the worst possible scenarios, and forecast how many people will be killed if a force five storm hit the island. People watch the newscasts, of course, even though they only want to know if the hurricane is coming their way and what time they should leave to be as far inland as possible before it hits.

The Weather Channel is important to people who live near the coast. Unlike tornadoes and mud slides, one can see in color graphs a hurricane approaching and listen to an experienced meteorologist explain how many miles per hour it is moving. Islanders also pray to The Weather Channel. I suppose this is because the God of the weather grew tired of relying on its collection of meteorological prophets to get the word out.

Most of us don't care much for meteorologists because they go on and on about what the climate is like on the other side of the country, when all we want to know is if we should take an umbrella outside. Recognizing the success of television evangelists, meteorologists pooled their resources and started The Weather Channel so that for twenty-four hours each day, they can broadcast the message of The Weather God.

People respond to The Weather God, too, normally by praying to The Weather Channel. When they see a hurricane heading for their area, they beseech The Weather God to turn the storm a bit in either direction so it can hit a beach they didn't like enough to move to or could not afford. "Please let it hit somewhere else," they pray.

If the storm continues, however, islanders give up on The Weather Channel and take matters into their own hands. Island bars begin promoting hurricane parties, where residents who do not wish to leave nail themselves inside a bar, get as drunk as possible, and ride out the storm. Hurricanes influence people to do things they would normally never consider.

A few months after I moved to Tybee, people began tracking hurricane Hugo with their free maps from McDonald's. Over the course of several days, the storm grew in speed and intensity. While the seas were still calm off Tybee—in fact people were swimming—the "beach-head" sailors knew that beyond the horizon the sea was dark, and whitecaps streaked along the surface like whipped cream. The wind was blowing far out in the sea, sixty or seventy miles per hour, fast enough to sweep a small child away.

Residents continued to chart their tracking maps and learned—to the dismay of everyone—that if Hugo continued on its present course, it would smash directly into Tybee Island. Some people began making ready, even though landfall was still several days away. The cautious ones can never be too prepared.

Over the next several days, The Weather Channel informed everyone that Hugo was still determined to visit Tybee Island. In fact, the twenty-four-hour weather reporters explained that if the storm continued on its present course, the city of Savannah would bear the brunt of landfall. Tybee Island did not even rate a mention, even though Hugo would have to pass through the island in order to reach Savannah. The civil defense unit warned residents to make ready for the storm and announced evacuation plans.

The day before Hugo was due to hit, the island was filled with activity. Residents loaded their prized possessions into vehicles and prepared to leave for the mainland. Janice loaded our station wagon with cherished photographs, certain books, the dog, clothes, and most anything else she could jam inside—including our three children.

She informed me that I was to obtain large sheets of plywood to board up the windows in our house. Because our house has so many windows, I replied that we would have to take out a second mortgage to purchase that much lumber. It quickly became apparent that I had no choice in the matter, and I ordered the wood.

Hugo was 200 miles offshore and headed straight toward Tybee when the plywood arrived. I left work early, rushed home, changed clothes, spent half-an-hour looking for a hammer, and prepared to secure the house. When I walked outside, several of my neighbors, with mixed drinks in their hands, milled around the stack of wood.

"What are you doing?" one asked.

"I'm going to board up my windows and secure the house for the hurricane," I explained, hoping they had come to help. Peering over their shoulders, however, I noticed that none of the other houses on the street had been boarded up.

"What are you going to do that for?" my neighbor asked, taking a sip from his drink and looking at me as though I had lost my mind.

"Because I don't want Hugo going through my living room," I responded, remembering that many of my neighbors had moved from somewhere else and likely did not realize the dangers of a hurricane.

"Well, that is not the way to get ready," he said, as though he were taking pity on me.

"I certainly think plywood has to be better than glass in protecting my house," I explained, growing frustrated at the lack of support from my neighbors.

"Look, if this hurricane is as strong as they say it is, the first thing that's going to happen is it will blow your roof off, then blow your windows out, and by then—if anything is left standing—the water surge will sweep your house off its foundation and carry it to downtown Savannah."

"What are you saying?" I asked, unable to comprehend that I could not secure my home against the fury of nature.

"What I'm saying is that Savannah will be a lot closer to the ocean after this storm hits."

I could not think of anything to say in response, so I asked if there was anything I should do.

"Your flood insurance paid up?" he asked. I said it was, and he responded: "Then you've done everything you can do. Here, let me fix you a going-away drink."

We walked across the street to his house where he mixed me a libation. Returning to the pile of plywood, he suggested I put up a "For Sale" sign and unload the useless materials before it was too late. I made the sign and, less than five minutes later, a pick-up truck whipped into my driveway, and the driver purchased the lumber. He told us he was returning from the sold-out lumber yards and still needed to protect his house.

"No problem," I told him, "my house is already as secure as it is going to be." We helped him load the lumber onto his truck.

Janice came outside and asked what had happened to our plywood and why I wasn't working. I confidently explained the realities of hurricane destruction, and—while I am not certain she was convinced—the evacuation horn sounded, and she rushed back inside to continue packing. I sat with my neighbors and sipped the drink. We prayed to The Weather Channel that Hugo would change its course before arriving at the Savannah River channel.

I was on Interstate 16 trying to get as far from the ocean as possible when I heard the news. When Hugo was sixty miles off Tybee's shore, it decided to go to Charleston. The Weather God had heard our prayers. I slowed down and prolonged the trip to my in-law's home in Middle Georgia, where we later watched the newscast of the destruction Hugo wrought on the South Carolina city.

Scenes of utter devastation were repeated on television throughout the day. At one point, a newscaster asked why anyone would want to live so close to the ocean when a hurricane can do this kind of damage at any time. I knew why. When the ocean calls, you can never leave for very long. We knew we would return to Tybee in spite of the danger of hurricanes or any other reason to stay away. It was our home.

I also thought of my new neighbors. Their calm resolve in the face of a hurricane was, I thought, a testimony to their love of the island. All they could do was to make certain the insurance was paid. Even if the storm had hit, washing their homes away and wiping out everything on the island, they would have come back.

Later, as the people in Charleston returned to the rubbish that used to be their homes, as they picked up waterlogged furniture and soaked photographs of their sons and daughters, they were asked why they bothered to return. "It's home" was the simple and earnest reply.

We know the risk of living here, and we're willing to take it. Many people shook their heads and did not understand the feelings of the Charlestonians, but I understood as I watched the washed-out neighbors help each other start again. No man is an island. We simply have the privilege of living on an island.

Tenth Street and the Valley of the Sea Chicken

Before the advent of Spanky's Beachside, with its outdoor bar and over-sized speakers blasting music toward the beach, most of the high school and college kids designated Tenth Street as their place to meet. Located in the middle of the island, the ocean side of Tenth Street is just long enough to have six houses placed on either side, the majority of which are summer homes to Savannah residents, only four serving as year-round residences.

These domiciles are varied in their design, with most constructed of wood and one of brick. All are two-story or placed on stilts, in compliance with flood laws, except for the lone brick edifice. Someone standing on the corner of Tenth and Butler and looking toward the ocean will see that all of the houses on the left are painted white, while the ones on the right are a hodgepodge of weather-worn colors.

Tenth Street was designated as a meeting place because of the beach, a broad strand filled with white, glimmering sand. At either end of the island are river channels, where the rushing water often sweeps away the shore or the constant winds of a northeaster (a storm with northeast winds) can cover the Sixteenth Street parking lot with what used to be the beach. This is not the case in the middle of the island. Protected by three sets of dunes, the sand does not blow away during a northeaster, nor do the rivers affect the shore.

Eighth and Fourteenth Streets can easily accommodate hundreds of sunbathers, with the lack of additional parking being the primary means of beach traffic control. The parking lots are located at the ends of the island where the beaches are washing away. The parking lots cannot be moved, so every few years the City of Tybee contracts with the Army Core of Engineers to move sand from the bottom of the ocean to the shores of Tybee. The result is that the ends of the island, with the least amount of beach but ample parking, are crowded and congested. The wide beach in the middle of the island, with very limited parking, is the least crowded.

Obviously, the beach off Tenth Street is far prettier than those at the ends of the island, where corn dog stands and parking lots distract from the beauty of the ocean. The folks who live on Tenth Street are well aware that their beach is the best one and are quite protective of it. Several decades ago, they were the first to lobby for and receive a dune crossover (a bridge over the mountains of sand and vegetation) to prevent people from trampling the dunes flat. There was only one dune when the crossover was built, and it amply carried visitors to the other side. Since then, however, two other series of dunes have developed, thereby dumping visitors into the middle of two sandy elevations. One must walk through the sand in order to reach the flat ocean beach.

Sand dunes serve as sentinels against salt, wind, and sun and offer a clear end for the beach while protecting against erosion. During the winter months, when the northeastern winds can blow over fifty miles per hour, the dunes grow to higher levels by collecting sand that blows. In the summer, the dunes absorb the sun's intense heat, and the ground temperature soars to 140 degrees. Visitors are encouraged to wear shoes when hiking across the dunes, for the grasses flourish in extra-thick and prickly sandspurs that can puncture bare feet. Tenth Street residents refer to this area as the Valley of the Sea Chicken, so named by resident Keith Smith.

Several years ago, Keith took a vacation from work and rented a house beside the ocean for a month. It was an enjoyable time for his family as they frolicked by the sea and generally retreated from the real world back in Savannah. When the month ended, he and Ellen decided their retreat was not over, so they took a year's sabbatical and stayed in the house beside the dunes. A gregarious and humorous person, Keith is a salesman in real life. Because he wasn't selling anything, Keith was quickly adopted by the other year-round residents of the street. One hot August day, we were standing on the crosswalk talking about how hot it was.

"What was the temperature today?" I asked.

"Ninety-five," he replied, "so hot The Breakfast Club could have shut off the grill and cooked breakfast on the sidewalk."

"That hot, uh?"

"Yep, and with no wind; there's no telling how many people died in the Valley of the Sea Chicken today."

"The what?" I asked.

Tenth Street and the Valley of the Sea Chicken

"You ain't never heard of the Valley of the Sea Chicken?"

I admitted that I had never heard of the place.

"This is the Valley of the Sea Chicken," he explained, looking toward the dunes. "Strange things happen here. It gets so hot during the day, whole families of tourists are swallowed up never to be heard from again. At night, people have a tendency to be swayed by the romantic lure of the dunes and, somehow—don't ask how—they lose their clothes. Passion takes over and people who come here at night do pretty strange things. They get confused and allow their primeval urges to take them over. Sometimes, they get so crazy, they act like a chicken, scratching in the sand with their feet and such."

"That's just because they have a sandspur stuck in their foot and are hopping around as they try to pull it out."

"That's the scientific explanation," he rationalized, "and doesn't distract from the fact they look awful silly jumping up and down like that."

I admitted some people did look pretty silly.

"Besides, the Valley of the Sea Chicken brings out other primeval urges, and people do things they would normally never be caught dead doing."

"Like what?" I asked.

"Well," he continued, "grown men and women will go to the bathroom in broad daylight for the whole world to see. They will leave the beach, where they have their chairs, radios, and coolers, being drawn to the dunes. Once in the Valley of the Sea Chicken, women will pull down their bathing suits and pee. I suppose it's an old ritual of communing with nature."

"That's because they have to go to the bathroom, and there aren't any around," I again explained. "They figure they can find some privacy in the dunes, and it's much more convenient than hopping in the car and driving a mile to the restrooms."

"Boy, you really have an analytical mind. You can try to explain all this if you want to, but it's not normal. I'm telling you the Valley of the Sea Chicken alters the way people think."

"Okay, give me another example."

"If there is a full moon, even stranger things can happen," he teased, smiling and enjoying his Stephen King version of the beach.

"Like what?" I nudged him on.

"Couples will be strolling down the beach at night, and suddenly the urge to enter the Valley of the Sea Chicken will overcome them. Entering the dunes, passion subdues them and when they leave, they normally leave some of their clothes or other objects of devotion to the Sea Chicken."

"Objects of devotion?" I asked.

"Yeah. Somehow the combination of a full moon and the Valley of the Sea Chicken causes them to lock their lips and roll around naked in the sand. Of course, sooner or later they roll into a patch of sandspurs, and the Sea Chicken gets his revenge for folks trampling all over his valley. After feeling his bite, they scream and collect their things as quickly as possible, but always seem to leave these gifts."

"Keith," I said, "you've been on sabbatical too long."

While he admitted this was probably true, he would not allow it to distract from his interpretation of the dunes. "Look, I live right next to the Valley of the Sea Chicken, and I've spent a lot of my time studying these things. During the day, I sit on my porch conducting research. At night Ellen and I will be in bed, and we hear all of the moaning and groaning from people who have been drawn into the Valley. It can get frightening."

A few weeks later, I had occasion to see for myself the powerful changes the Valley of the Sea Chicken can have on perfectly normal people. Gil, a friend of mine for twenty years, brought his family to Tybee for a weekend. He is a very intelligent, dignified, and scholarly minister who lived outside Washington, D.C. at the time. Like most members of the clergy, he dresses formally, speaks with a clear diction, and carries himself with much distinction. Also like most clergy, Gil is not a frequent visitor to the beach. Whenever I have visited our nation's capital or most any place away from the ocean, it seems that white people in those places are much whiter than those who live near the coast; Gil was certainly one when he arrived.

"You need some sun," I immediately told him.

Now Gil is pretty open-minded about many things, but sometimes he reads too much. He began to share all of the recently-released studies concerning skin cancer. It is difficult to stop a preacher from talking once he starts, and I had to allow the lecture to run its course before I informed him of the discovery of suntan lotion, hats, and other ways to protect oneself from the harmful ultraviolet rays. While he may have still been suspicious, he agreed to accompany me on a walk down the beach.

After coating Gil with lotion and finding him a baseball cap, I began to search for some flip-flops he could wear, which took a few minutes because I never wear them. I have learned if I walked barefoot beginning in March, my feet will grow accustomed to the hot pavement of Tenth Street, the hellish temperature of the sand dunes, and even the sandspurs on which I occasionally step.

As I handed him the flip-flops, he asked, "Aren't you going to wear any?"

"No, I don't need them," I explained.

"Then I don't need any either." The Sea Chicken was beginning to influence his thinking, but I did not notice what was happening. I explained that I had built up an endurance for hot pavement and sand, but he remained firm.

When we were in college, Gil and I were very competitive with each other. We competed in class, on the tennis courts, and in playing cards and basketball. Twenty years later, we still engage in adolescent competitive behavior. I knew there was no use in trying to convince him to wear the shoes, so we began our trek to the beach.

We had not gone half a block before the Sea Chicken's power began to repress all of his normal traits. First, he began to dance in the middle of the street. His feet began to hop, skip, and jump as we made our way toward the ocean. Sitting in the coolness of their porches, my neighbors watched my friend's strange behavior. I tried to appear normal.

Then Gil screamed. The Sea Chicken was beginning to overpower him. My neighbors had seen the sad spectacle before and appeared to be sympathetic. Next, obviously trying to break the influence of the Sea Chicken, he bolted for the grass in one of the yards of my neighbors. I yelled words of warning, but it was too late. He ran into the grass, only to stop in a rather large patch of sandspurs. Again he screamed in torment.

In anguish, he raced toward the crosswalk. I yelled out words of warning but, again, I was too late. The sun dries out the wood used to construct the bridges, and splinters abound. They stuck into the bottom of his feet beside the sandspurs. His suffering was becoming unbearable, and he darted into the Valley of the Sea Chicken.

"No!" I called, not having informed him of how hot the sand is during the month of August. I couldn't see him, but I heard his repeated howls. The Sea Chicken had consumed him. It was also beginning to affect me; I did not express concern and empathy as a normal friend would. Instead, I started laughing. The Sea Chicken is very powerful.

When I finally crossed through the valley, Gil was standing in the ocean's edge, and steam was rising out of the water. We walked a ways, but his feet hurt so badly we returned home by another route. Once home, his feet were so seriously blistered that he didn't leave the house for two days. I told him about the Valley of the Sea Chicken. As soon as he was able to walk, he packed his family into the car and left. He has never again visited Tybee.

Even if the Tenth Street dunes were not the home of the Sea Chicken, its residents are different from other islanders. Most are only summertime occupants of their beach houses; hence they bring much of Savannah's culture and values with them to Tybee. This is probably the reason Tenth Street residents are the only group to have their own Fourth of July parade. For most islanders, the midsummer holiday is just another day at the beach. On Tenth Street, however, it is a unique celebration that has been a tradition for more than two decades.

In many ways, the Fourth of July on Tenth Street is no different from a host of other communities across the country. Houses proudly display the American flag. Cookouts and special parties are planned. Family members travel far and wide to reunite for the celebration. Most of Savannah's citizens pack their coolers and cars and travel to Tybee for the day. The island is packed and, if the tide happens to be high in the afternoon, it can be difficult to find any sand not occupied. But as the afternoon wears on, some folks leave, and others may arrive and take their place.

Tybee sponsors an annual fireworks display when night falls, and, from the right vantage spots, one can also view the celebrations on River Street in Savannah and on Hilton Head Island. Islanders who watch three displays at one time spend a great deal of time turning around in every direction. At the end of the show, many of them are too dizzy to drive and wander to the closest party they can find. The island's bars plan special activities such as cookouts, bikini contests, and live music; so the merrymaking lasts well into the night.

In the middle of such typical activities is the Tenth Street celebration. At five o'clock in the afternoon, residents gather in front of the Freeman's house, where specially-designed T-shirts are sold. Small American flags are distributed to anyone who did not bring their own. A few folks decorate their boats or trucks as though they are parade floats, and the smaller children climb aboard.

A couple of hundred people from the surrounding streets and lanes eventually arrive to participate. Drinks are fixed for those who did not bring their own. By 5:30 someone stumbles toward Butler Avenue, and the march begins, which sometimes coincides with the precise time that several thousand folks are trying to leave the island. The procession can bring traffic to a complete halt.

Tenth Street and the Valley of the Sea Chicken

One year the traffic was at a deadlock while 200 people took up two lanes of the highway, waving flags and singing "Yankee Doodle Dandy." Eventually, the Tybee Island Police Department dispatched an officer to determine the cause of the problem and free up the traffic.

As we marched, we heard the sirens blasting from a distance draw nearer. When the patrolman pulled alongside the parade, several people cheered and commented how nice it was to have a police escort. With the siren wailing and the blue lights flashing, he pulled his car off the road, blocking the unknown parade route and cutting off the procession. As he climbed out of the car, he demanded to know who was in charge.

Several of us gathered around and politely asked, "What is the problem officer?"

"What's the problem? Can't you see what you're doing to traffic? People are trying to leave the island, and you are obstructing them from doing so."

We admitted this was indeed true, but most of these people were tourists who were inhibiting the progress of our parade. We asked if he could do something to get them out of our way.

"Get them out of your way?!" he almost screamed. "They're not the problem! You are!"

Fortunately Tenth Street is the summer residence of several attorneys and politicians who can immediately recognize when their special talents were needed.

"Excuse me officer," they said, "but we are tax-paying citizens of Tybee Island. In fact, we contribute to your salary and are proud to do so, but this is our island; and these people have come all the way from Savannah to impede our celebration of the birth of this great country."

"Uh-huh," the confused cop replied.

Figuring they had done yet another masterful job of utterly confusing the public, the attorneys and politicians looked at one another and smiled.

"Well then," the surprising courteous officer said, "I guess the only thing I need to see is your parade permit."

This simple request was followed by a pronounced and deep silence. The attorneys and politicians faded into the crowd, which suddenly seemed smaller than before.

"You do have a parade permit, don't you?"

No one spoke, although several people began digging in their pockets in hopes of finding an extra one.

"Well, I suppose I'm going to have to cite you for parading without a permit," said the policeman as he pulled out his book of tickets. "Now, who is in charge?"

Several persons began speaking at once. Some explained the Tenth Street tradition; others cussed; and one wanted to fight the cop, claiming he was un-American. The patrolman grinned and waved his arms.

"Just carry the parade over to some of the back streets, and I'll let it slide. The traffic can flow, and you all can continue your little celebration."

Everyone seemed to agree that this was a good solution, and we proceeded back home on Lovel Avenue. It is probably the only time in American history that a Fourth of July parade has been pulled over by a policeman. While I am certain this *could* happen somewhere else, it seems typical for Tybee and characteristic of Tenth Street.

Like the Valley of the Sea Chicken, strange things can also happen at night on the other end of Tenth Street. During the summer months, the population of the island triples, and the hotels are filled with tourists. Many people stay up late into the night visiting the Sixteenth Street bars at the south end of the island or the bars at the north end.

Valley of the Sea Chicken

Tenth Street and the Valley of the Sea Chicken

Tenth Street is in the middle of the two collections of saloons. Customers often leave the bars at one end of the island and walk up or down Butler Avenue to those at the other end. Islanders grow adept at ignoring the snippets of conversations they hear as people walk past their open windows. Sometimes, however, Tenth Street residents see things that no one else has the opportunity to view and few believe when these events are reported.

In the middle of one night, the ringing of the telephone woke me from a deep slumber. Sleepily I stumbled toward the wall phone in the kitchen. I mumbled greetings as I picked up the receiver.

"Look out your window," the voice of my neighbor instructed.

"For heaven's sake, it's 2:30 in the morning!" I said in frustration.

"I know, but you've got to see this. Look out of your window."

I stared out the window into my front yard. Because our house is on the corner of Tenth and Butler Avenue, and this is the middle of the island, a bench had been placed in the yard to accommodate those who need bus transportation. I hated the bench and had moved it several times across the street to someone else's yard, but the bus company always brought it back.

Once Jeremy and Kristen, two of my children, helped me hide the offensive fixture by moving it to a back street. It was made of heavy wood affixed to even heavier concrete, so it took us quite some time to move it. It was back several days later, so I gave up, figuring it would always be a part of our outdoor decor. I never knew, however, that the bench was sometimes used at night. As I stared out the window that night, I saw upon the much-hated bench a man who was sound asleep and wearing nothing but his tennis shoes.

At that moment, the flashing blue lights of a Tybee Island Police Department patrol car screeched to a halt beside the bench. The officer had not turned on the siren. I suppose he did not want to awaken the sleeping figure, because the body did not move. The vehicle's door flew open, and out stepped one of Tybee's finest. He stood and surmised that while the situation did not need back ups, a special tool was necessary. Leaning over and reaching into his patrol car, he pulled out a golf club. It looked like a nine iron.

The flashing blue lights must have awakened the man, or perhaps his unconscious mind detected the presence of another being. Regardless, the naked sleeping man awoke, saw the officer, bolted up, and darted into the dark of Tenth Street toward the Valley of the Sea Chicken. The alert policeman chased after him, waving the nine iron over his head. The car was left in the middle of Butler Avenue with the door open, engine running, and blue lights flashing.

"You see all that?" my neighbor asked.

I had almost forgotten I was holding the telephone receiver in my hand and that he was watching the same event from his side of the street. I imagined him standing beside his window, looking much like myself—in his underwear, hair askew from rubbing against his pillow, and a telephone in his hand.

"Yeah," I said, "I saw it. Unbelievable!"

"Well, good night."

"Good night," I replied and returned to my bed.

The following morning at The Breakfast Club, the officer was seated at the counter, drinking coffee and reading the newspaper. I took the stool next to him and explained that I had observed the crime on Tenth Street that night.

"Did you ever catch him?" I asked.

"Nope," he calmly replied. "Chased him down the beach, but he must have run into the dunes. It was so dark last night I couldn't see a thing, so he got away."

Ben, a fisherman who works as a waiter to support his habit, placed my coffee in front of me, and I gratefully paused long enough to take several swallows before I continued with the question that was on my mind.

"What were you going to do with that golf club?"

He smiled as he stood to pay his bill and asked me what I thought he was going to do.

I assured him I had no idea.

Grinning, he said, "I was going to tee off. What else?"

Little has changed on Tenth Street in the seven years we have lived here. Keith and Ellen's sabbatical ran out after five years, and they moved to a nice condominium on Wilmington Island that he refers to as the projects.

Two of the houses on the street burned, and thousands of people spent a cold Sunday afternoon traveling to Tybee merely to watch the blaze. The owners rebuilt their houses almost precisely as they had been. The city council recently voted to replace the short, single crossover with one that will stretch over all three sets of dunes. We skipped the Fourth of July parade the year the houses burned because no one felt right about having it without all residents of the street.

Tenth Street and the Valley of the Sea Chicken

The police officer with the nine iron has since taken a job elsewhere, probably as a golf instructor. The hated bench was finally moved from our yard when someone determined that it was utilized more for sleeping than for waiting on the bus.

The Valley of the Sea Chicken still reigns supreme in the dunes, although the new crosswalk will likely prevent many tourists from experiencing its wrath. Tenth Street is a strange street on a strange island. The only thing stranger are the people on the other streets.

Tenth Street

43

Bubba Ball and the Phantom

Jeremy mastered T-ball in Louisville, where the game took place by a water tower beside the Ohio River. A massive open field surrounding the water tower had been converted to eight or ten diamonds. According to the schedule, Jeremy would arrive with several thousand other children, each transported by several thousand parents, all completely overwhelming the ball fields. Games consisted of one child after another stepping up to the T and whacking the daylights out of it. Some children actually hit the ball on top of the T, but most of them smacked the plastic stand itself.

I suspect most children were staring at their fathers or mothers who were screaming rapid fire instructions and encouragement. Consequently, when they finally swung the bat, it would hit the T and knock it over, causing the ball to roll toward the pitcher's mound. According to the rules, that was not a hit; so while the coach tried to prevent the batter from completely circling the bases, the parents collectively groaned because the process would start over again. Most T-ball games lasted several days.

Jeremy was advanced far beyond the other children, who were most likely fulfilling the failed ambitions of a father or mother who had missed the thrill of knocking a T over and racing his or her coach around the bases. He and I practiced daily in the backyard as we prepared for the season. He was a pure hitting machine from the same state that produced Ty Cobb and Henry Aaron.

I had confidence in Jeremy's ability and, having been a former player myself, knew not to embarass him by yelling instructions when he stepped up to the plate. Instead, before he entered the batter's box, I quietly reminded him to do what great hitters do when approaching the plate. Jeremy smiled and confidently walked to the T. His coach, still trying to catch his breath after chasing the previous batter all the way to second base, did not appreciate my son's approach.

Taking two practice swings as most professional ballplayers do, Jeremy then spit toward the pitcher's mound as a sign of disrespect for the opposing pitcher. Of course, in T-ball there is no opposing pitcher. So while the act was utterly meaningless, the coach at least knew that Jeremy meant business. Finally, he reached down and grabbed his crotch. Seeing this display, his mother yelled, "Mike, Get over here right now!"—which distracted Jeremy's concentration.

He hit the T with all of his might. The sound was like plywood crashing against a plate of glass. The ball rolled slowly toward the pitcher's mound. Jeremy and I both looked at his mother in disgust. The coach retrieved the ball and set it upon the T again. His mother held her tongue as Jeremy repeated the ritual, then he hit the ball squarely, driving it into the outfield. This boy could play ball in spite of his mother.

He later progressed to Midget League in Louisville. I was an assistant coach for the team and threw batting practice and was also the pitcher during the game. Midget League ball is only slightly more advanced than T-ball, as the coaches are the pitchers. Jeremy would dutifully spit at me whenever he batted, but would tell me as we drove home he had not meant it. He mastered this game, too.

Our move to Tybee coincided with Jeremy's advancement to the big time: Little League—with real pitching, coaches who stayed off the field, and the chance to steal bases. The sign in front of City Hall announced the dates to sign up for the new season. We completed the necessary paperwork and obtained the required additional insurance. We had been practicing in the backyard for weeks. Jeremy's arm was strong, his glove was well-oiled, and his confidence was soaring. He was ready to introduce himself as the slugger from Louisville.

The day came for the first practice. We drove to J. C. Park where the diamond revealed why baseball is sometimes referred to as a sandlot game. I had never paused to consider what a baseball field would look like on an island, but seeing it for the first time made me appreciate the valiant efforts of the recreation department workers.

Truckloads of red dirt had been hauled in from some other part of the state. The grass was well-watered, and most of the outfield was green. Lights had been installed on massive poles surrounding the playing field. Bleachers could accommodate several hundred spectators. Still, sand was everywhere.

Bubba Ball and the Phantom

It blew on top of the imported dirt, choked the well-watered grass, formed small mounds around some of the light poles, and dominated the area surrounding the bleachers.

While the field was not what we had expected, it was still pretty decent-looking—if taken within its broader context. Nearby a playground was set up for younger children to enjoy while their parents watched the ballgames. An asphalt jogger's track meandered its way around the circumference of the park. A pond was the home of several wild-looking, but well-fed, geese and ducks. Tall marsh grass grew in certain areas with cattails watching over the field. There were bridges to stand on to watch the animals swim as they begged for bread or crackers. The sound of waves could be heard crashing onto the shore, and the salt air was pleasant to breath. To this day the park is nice, even with sand on the baseball field.

Having approved of the playing field, it was time to meet the coach. As we approached, a team was practicing. Unlike the loud parents in Louisville, those observing were respectful of the coach volunteering his time, talent, and money for their son's athletic development. The rear end of the instructor came into view. He wore dark blue, spandex pants that were literally bursting at the seams and a sleeveless light blue shirt. The posterior was that of a man with a real beer gut. A yellow cap sat on top of his closely cropped grey hair. He was intensely scrutinizing a batter at the plate.

The pitcher hurled the ball with all of his might, emitting a loud grunt as he made the release. The batter's muscles flexed, the bat went still, and he swung to make connection with the ball. He drove it to the outfield and, obviously proud of this accomplishment, began to jump up and down proclaiming, "I did it! I did it!" Of course, he should have been running to first base. At this point, Jeremy and I learned how the coach instructed.

"Run you little son of a bitch! Run!" The woman's voice dominated the entire park, rattling several windows in the houses across the street.

As the coach took a step toward the lad, screaming at him to run, the boy dropped the bat and ran toward first base as though his life depended on it.

"That's the way to run! If you don't run like that, I'll kick your ass to kingdom come. When a player gets a hit, he runs!"

Standing safely on first base, the little boy fearfully nodded his head up and down at a very fast pace.

One of the parents uneasily rose from the bleachers and began to make his way toward the coach. I assumed it was the boy's father, who—as I would have done—wanted to address the way the coach talked to his son.

Leaning over to fetch the discarded bat, the coach saw the parent while he was still ten feet away and said, "Sit your ass back down while I'm coaching, or I'll kick your ass from here to kingdom come and back again." The father hesitated a moment, probably wondering if he could take the woman or not, then meekly returned to the bleachers without ever saying a word.

Jeremy and I looked at each other at the same time. Fear was in his eyes, and I must have had the same expression as we both immediately turned around and went to the car. Inside the safety of locked steel and glass, he told me that he did not want to play for a woman coach.

"I know what you mean, son," I replied. "They just don't know as much about baseball."

"Yeah," he nodded, "let's see if we can find another team." We quickly drove away.

Fortunately, a group of intimidated fathers had decided to start their own team as an alternative to the team sponsored by the City of Tybee. I attended the inaugural meeting of this group. There I learned about the city team. The coach was named Georgeanna, and her brother, Bubba, contributed a good deal of time and money to the team. It played in the YMCA league, which did not adhere to the rules established in the Little League of America rule book. The differences seemed to be minor.

"Well," I said after hearing this, "I want my son to play real baseball and not this Midget League stuff." They asked what Midget League was. I explained that I had recently moved from Louisville, and everyone seemed to understand.

The following day, we asked The Breakfast Club owner if he would be interested in sponsoring a baseball team. "If they're called the Cubs and have uniforms that look like the Chicago Cubs, I will," Jordy delightfully replied.

So during my first summer on Tybee, I became a founder and assistant coach of a revolutionary baseball team. The City of Tybee did not offer real baseball, had a woman coach, and teams were taught the fundamentals of Bubba Ball. "What's that?" I asked when I was first told of the approach. Bubba Ball is the equivalent of a Wall Street approach to baseball. While the female coach I had observed used fear and intimidation as a motivation to excel in athletics, Bubba used greed.

Bubba Ball and the Phantom

"Hey," he would call out during batting practice, "get a hit, and I'll give you a dollar." This statement was his entire philosophy in summation. "Catch that pop fly, and I'll give you a dollar. Throw the other team out, and I'll give you a dollar. Win this game, and the pizza's on me. Have a winning season, and I'll take you whitewater rafting," he would yell from the bench.

I'm not certain how many boys learned the fundamentals of baseball, but I suspect Bubba Ball instilled the notion that winning means money, and the majority of his former players went on to become successful inside traders and agents for professional athletes.

The Tybee Island Recreation Department was angry with us that year. Because the City of Savannah boasted "real" baseball, the Tybee Cubs enrolled in that league. We proved we were not ready for real baseball, however, and went on to have a losing season. The boys seemed to have a good time, though.

During this time, I made a habit to arrive at The Breakfast Club early each morning and report to Jordy the progress of the Cubs. He was an enthusiastic backer who offered words of encouragement as the season wore on.

"How's the team doing?" he would yell over his shoulder as he scrambled eggs, buttered toast, rolled an omelet, and did several thousand other things at the same time.

"Not too well," I dutifully reported.

"Well, don't worry. They have great uniforms!"

As I opened my newspaper and sipped my coffee, from over my shoulder I heard, "You would have done better if you'd kept the damn team with the city. Tybee always has a baseball team, but because you had to go start your own, the Tybee recreation department had to drop theirs."

The former coach of the team was speaking. Wearing the same stretch blue pants and the same light blue sleeveless shirt, she commanded my attention. I noticed her hands were black, and she was not wearing her usual baseball cap. Other than that, it appeared she had not changed clothes since earlier that summer.

"We just wanted to play real baseball," I stammered.

She was an imposing figure who would pop or play with the ten or twenty rubber bands on her wrist.

"Give me a fried-egg-jack-cheese sandwich," she said to Jordy, who immediately cracked an egg on the grill.

"Mayonnaise on it, Georgeanna?" he asked.

"Hell no! Butter!" she barked.

When she got the sandwich, white cheese was dripping from the bread. When she took a bite, a bridge of cheese connected her mouth with the sandwich in her hands.

"You live on Tenth Street."

Looking to see whether or not she was talking to me, I saw she had made an utter mess on the counter with crushed cigarette butts spilling from the ashtray. She had built a mountain of empty Sweet-and-Low packets and had obviously missed her coffee cup with the white powder.

"How do you know that?" I asked.

Holding up her black hands she asked, "How in the hell do you think your newspaper gets in your driveway?"

I told her that I had never really given it any thought, but assumed some kid worked as the paper boy.

"No some kid don't work as the paper boy; you have me to thank. How would a kid get off the island at one o'clock in the morning? Ride his bicycle?"

I said I had not given much thought to that either, but assumed the newspaper employed someone to bring bundled editions to the island where they were distributed.

"Shows how much you know," she said with strings of cheese dripping from her mouth. The paper won't come all the way to the island, and I have to meet them at one o'clock. That's why you have your paper on time."

Not knowing what else to say, I thanked her and commented that I had no idea getting the paper delivered to the island was so difficult.

As I continued to arrive at The Breakfast Club early in the morning, I often found myself sitting with Georgeanna. She always looked the same: hands covered with black newspaper print, the same clothes, and a personality that could cause Attila the Hun to back down in fear. She took a liking to me, though. I could tell because when she entered The Breakfast Club, she hit me on the back with a rolled-up newspaper. This was as close as she came to ever showing affection.

I learned that Georgeanna had been married once for a few years, had borne several children, and her ex-husband still worked for her delivering the heavy Sunday editions of the paper. I assume this arrangement is either a condition of the divorce, or—like the rest of us—he is scared to death she will beat the hell out of him if he quits. It was hard not to think such things about Georgeanna. She simply looked mean, sounded angry, and greeted people by hitting them.

Another of the morning regulars at The Breakfast Club was a retired military man named Grover. He and Georgeanna had a special greeting for one another. Grover was a gruff enough person in his own right. Born and raised in Elijay, Georgia, he prided himself on being a racist and told me once that he had raised his children to be racist. Whenever Georgeanna entered The Breakfast Club he would bark, "Hello, you old goat!" She would reply, "Morning Grouch," and slap him on the back with a rolled-up newspaper. While there was genuine fondness between them, no one dared question those exchanges. Either one of them was likely to knock you off your stool, and there was always the possibility they would gang up on you.

I began to notice Georgeanna at her work, driving a pale blue-and-white pickup truck at thirty miles per hour down the short island streets. In the darkness, papers would fly out of her windows and land at the doorstep of her customers. Her aim at fast speeds became our next conversation.

Before walking into The Breakfast Club one rainy morning, I dipped my perfectly good paper in a puddle and soaked it completely. Entering the restaurant, I placed it in front of her and said she had missed. Instead of the laughter I expected to hear from the others, the place filled with an uneasy silence. Jordy even stopped. I stood behind Georgeanna with a sudden impending sense of doom.

"I never miss," she said without turning around.

"Well," I stammered, "you did this time; my paper is soaked."

Slowly turning on her stool, I suddenly felt I was on the set of a Clint Eastwood movie and had been cast opposite the star. She looked into my eyes, and ever so slightly a grin graced her face. This was a sign that everyone else could laugh, and they did. Jordy resumed the thousand different things he was doing, and Georgeanna told me where I could get a dry newspaper.

"It took a lot of guts to pull that joke," she said as she turned to the morning mess she was making on the counter.

I made the mistake of thinking this event signified some entry on my part into the complete confidence of the gang at The Breakfast Club, a belief dispelled a few weeks later.

On a rainy Friday night, my wife and I drove the car to the end of Tenth Street to have dinner with some friends. At the evening's end, the rain had ceased, so Janice and I decided to leave the car, walk home, and retrieve it the following morning.

Because I am an early riser, I was dressed and out of the house by 6:30 A.M. The sun was just beginning to show signs of waking up as I stepped onto Tenth Street and made my way to the car. It is always quiet at this time of day. Most people are still sleeping, so there are no televisions or radios blaring, children gleefully screaming as they arrive for a day at the beach, or traffic. The only noise is the constant sound of the ocean hugging the shore. The only people to be seen are the tourists who are determined to see the sun rise over the ocean or the few others, like myself, who think this is the best part of the day.

The walk became a mini-celebration of God's creation. Once humanity shuts off its roaring engines, ringing telephones, and endless conversations, I can remember the power behind the words of the prophet: "Be still and know that I am God." The still of the morning or the dead of night is the time of day when God probably takes walks around the world.

As I was thinking these thoughts, a pair of headlights turned onto Tenth Street, and the roar of an engine drowned out the crashing of the waves. I stepped to the side of the road as the headlights drew closer. I must not have moved quickly enough, however, for they appeared before I made it to the curb. The vehicle was flying! Just as it passed, I stepped onto the curb. Thinking I was safe, I turned to see an object flying past my head.

"Get out of the damn way!" Georgeanna screamed as she roared by.

A rolled-up newspaper alone hitting the human body can hurt. If that same object is thrown from a vehicle moving at thirty-five miles per hour, however, it is probably lethal.

At the end of the street, Georgeanna did a U-turn without slowing down and delivered the paper to the houses on the other side of the street. I could not help but ponder how many people wondered what really happened to their cat or dog when they woke to find their pet in a comatose state in the front yard beside the newspaper. I asked that question of Georgeanna after she popped me on the back when she entered The Breakfast Club.

"I told you," she explained, "I don't miss."

"You almost took my head off!" I said, explaining to everyone what had happened that morning.

"If I had wanted to take your head off, I would have," she blandly explained.

"Oh, come on Georgeanna, no one is that perfect. You make it sound as though you're a comic book superhero stopping crime all over the island! Armed with nothing but the morning news, cleverly disguised as a delivery person, it's Paper Woman."

Everyone laughed, including Georgeanna. Two members of the Tybee Island Police Department were seated nearby and explained that Georgeanna had prevented more crimes than anyone else on the island. "Whenever she sees an open door or strangers at someone's house, she lets us know quickly. There have been many times when we have checked these things out, and we have caught someone doing something they weren't supposed to."

"I don't believe it," I said, not so much because I did not think it was true, but because no one seemed particularly interested in how my obituary would read if Georgeanna did decide to take my head off. "Man killed by rolled-up newspaper" the headlines would scream, before describing how it had been thrown at a fast speed at an innocent bystander.

"Sit down!" Georgeanna commanded. "I've already told you I don't miss."

I sat down, humbled at the morning's turn of events and the sad fact that no one took my version seriously. Georgeanna was gracious, however, as she suggested we split breakfast. Before I could decline, she ordered a hash brown omelet with ham, cheese, broccoli, and mushrooms. I told her that I did not know what she had just ordered. She told me to shut up because it was good.

Jordy placed the hash browns and other ingredients on the grill. After they simmered in butter for several minutes, he spread the ham, broccoli, and mushrooms on top of the hash browns. They cooked a few more minutes before he put some cheese on top. When the cheese melted, he flipped one-half of the concoction on top of the other. Elegantly rolling the whole thing on a plate, I had to admit that, while it was different, it looked good. Georgeanna carefully divided the "omelet" into two equal portions and slid a plate in front of me, before immediately taking a bite. Cheese dripped from the corner of her mouth.

Now I know what I like, and my wife has accused me of being a picky eater and unwilling to try new things. Looks can often be deceiving I told myself as I hesitated, not really wanting to try anything new that morning. Georgeanna noticed my reluctance and stopped eating long enough to offer words of encouragement.

"Look, I told you, it's good. Now eat!" she demanded.

Given a clear choice between choking down the food or being choked by Georgeanna, I stuffed a forkful into my mouth. It was delicious. Noticing my taste bud's approval, Georgeanna smiled and stated she had already told me it was good. I should believe her from now on. I cleaned my plate, not from fear, but in appreciation for a new delicacy.

A few weeks later, I was sitting next to Georgeanna when she suddenly ordered twenty breakfast meals to go. Jordy took the information in stride, even though it meant he had a thousand and twenty things to do at one time.

"Who died?" he asked, while moving at the speed of light.

"Mrs. Vinings," she replied as she crushed her cigarette, missing the ashtray and grinding the butt into a napkin.

"Same deal?" Jordy asked.

"Yeah, same deal."

Everyone else seemed to consider this strange order as normal. They continued sipping coffee and quietly talking with each other. Georgeanna calmly drank her coffee and made her morning mess.

"Why are you ordering twenty breakfast meals to go because Mrs. Vinings died?" I asked.

"Hush," she snapped, shooting a glance at the others seated around the counter, "not so loud." No one seemed to care that we were talking.

"Have you ever heard of the phantom?" she whispered.

The phantom is well-known on Tybee. Whenever someone is ill, a package will be found at his or her door one morning. It will contain a small toy or a stuffed animal, perhaps some fresh fruit, and a card that will simply be signed, "The Fantom." When someone dies, breakfast is delivered to the home on the day of the funeral for the entire family and anyone else who happens to be staying at the house. On Christmas mornings, bags of fruit and toys are found hanging on the doors of the homes of sick and poor people. Each bag bears the signature: "The Fantom." Everyone knows about the phantom, but no one will ever say who it is. I told Georgeanna I had indeed heard of the phantom.

"Why don't you make yourself useful and write the card," she demanded, handing me a pen and a sympathy card.

"What should I write?" I asked.

"How the hell should I know? You're the writer!"

Bubba Ball and the Phantom

I didn't quite know how to take this. So I began to write how the gang at The Breakfast Club felt bad about Mrs. Vinings' death and wanted to do something but couldn't think of anything appropriate and that perhaps the breakfast being delivered on a day filled with grief might convey the fact we were sending our love and were there for them when they returned from the funeral. When I finished I handed the card back to Georgeanna, who promptly read it. A smile came to her face.

"That's good," she said softly.

Jordy announced that the meals were ready, and I helped Georgeanna carry them to her truck. Mountains of bundled newspapers had to be shifted around until there was room for the meals. Once secured, she told me that if I ever said anything about this to anyone at all, she would kick my ass to kingdom come and back again. I promised I would never say a word.

Over the next several weeks. Georgeanna's knee began to give her problems, and she began using a crutch to assist her in walking. When we asked, she told us she had already been to the doctor, who informed her that surgery was necessary. Because she had no health insurance, she could not afford to take time off to have the surgery. After awhile, she became angry over the fact that she had a crutch and threw it away, saying she would rather live with the pain than the inconvenience.

When Christmas came, she told me she needed my help to do her job. Her knee was bothering her too much to make all of her deliveries. I told her that I already had a job and couldn't help her deliver newspapers.

"That ain't what I'm talking about," she snapped. "Come here." Slowly, in obvious discomfort, she stood and led me outside to her truck. In the back were forty or fifty red mesh bags filled with fruit and candy canes and, in some, toys. She began pulling several bags out and handing them to me. When she finished, she sat on the gate and exhaled loudly as she tried to catch her breath.

"Now the names are on the bags," she explained. "All of these folks live close to you. All you got to do is hang them on the door. Be sure it's early in the morning or late at night when you make the delivery. It's no big deal. I know you get up early. Make sure nobody sees you, and if you ever tell anyone about this . . ."

"I know," I interrupted, "you'll kick my ass to kingdom come and back again."

Not anticipating I would know the threat by heart, Georgeanna appeared to be at a loss for words and paused without saying anything. She waited until I had placed the packages in my car, and we both returned to The Breakfast Club. I was sure everyone had watched the exchange take place but, when we entered, no one said a word, as they all seemed to be intensely studying their coffee or newspapers. Everyone on Tybee knows who the phantom is, of course, but no one will dare discuss it because they are scared to death that she will kick their ass from here to kingdom come and back again.

On Christmas morning, the regulars showed up at The Breakfast Club at nine o'clock. Jordy and the crew prepared their special holiday feast for the regulars and anyone else who might be stuck on Tybee during the holiday. Everyone enjoyed this because it allowed those who start most every day of their lives together to celebrate Christmas in the same way. Georgeanna entered after she finished delivering the newspapers. She never has a day off, even on Christmas. When I wished her a happy holiday, she snapped, "Yeah, right, you too."

Then she pulled me aside and asked if all of my deliveries had been made. I assured her they had.

"Good," she said, "I'd hate for someone to go without on Christmas. You go and have a good day."

"What are you going to do today?" I asked her.

"Go to bed," she answered. "What else am I supposed to do? If I don't get some rest, you won't have your newspaper tomorrow."

I nodded my head and imagined her collapsing onto her bed as soon as she got home. I felt sorry for her. She worked all the time to make certain that everyone had their papers, taking great pride in how well she did her job. She never had a day off and had very little to show for her efforts. On the other hand, she seemed to know more about the spirit of Christmas than most anyone else on the island, but did not want anyone to know about her secret deliveries. She deserved something, but everyone was so frightened of her that no one dared to give her any gifts.

"Oh no, I'm not going to bed," she interrupted my thoughts. "I've got to help Bubba. He's bought a pile of ball uniforms he's giving to some damn kids downtown. I promised I would help him sort them."

"How many did he buy?" I asked.

"Hell, I don't know. Several hundred. He says there are a lot of project kids who need some. It'll take us all damn morning."

"Jordy," she yelled, "give me a fried-egg-jack-cheese sandwich."

Bubba Ball and the Phantom

Even though there was a special menu that day, which did not include special orders, he prepared it anyway. At least there was one person who recognized that Georgeanna merited something special every once in a while, especially on Christmas morning, when she was between deliveries.

Last Rites and First Rights

Tybee is such a small island that the need for automobiles is not especially pronounced. Most everyone has a car, of course, as this is the twentieth century and automatic convenience and instant gratification have become the primary goals of life. For those who choose to ride a bicycle, however, it only takes a bit longer to reach one's destination. Even if someone happens to be walking, it usually takes about half-an-hour to get from the southernmost end of the island to the end of Highway 80, the Tybee road. On an island this small, most everything is convenient regardless of one's mode of transportation.

The grocery store is located on the middle of the island, so everyone can get there in a matter of minutes. When the post office relocated several years ago from the south end to another section of the island, most folks commented that it was a shame they would never have cause to visit the Sixteenth Street area again. Sixteenth Street boasts the island's small commercial district, consisting of a one-half block of bars, a video arcade, a bondsman's office, tacky T-shirt shops, a small kiddies fair, a couple of cheap hotels, several hamburger and corn dog stands, and Chu's Department Store.

Chu's is the main reason islanders bother to go to Sixteenth Street at all. In the fifties, sixties, and seventies, Chu's seemed to have almost anything a customer could reasonably desire to purchase. It had a hardware department, suntan lotion, toys, bathing suits, clothing, groceries, and a coffee shop. In the eighties, however, Chu's experienced a decline. While it still has more of a choice than any other nearby establishment, most items seem to have been stocked in the late fifties and are covered with a layer of dust. In spite of the degeneration, Chu's offers people the choice of paying a higher price for a piece of elbow pipe rather than leaving the island. Most residents are loyal supporters of Chu's.

The rest of Sixteenth Street, as well as the parking lot, is commonly referred to as the "combat zone." The huge parking lot, coupled with a number of bars, is a drinker's delight. Kitten's Corner is a bar that tries to be a striptease club, but cannot get a license from the city, so the bikini-clad waitresses mainly serve drinks and dreams. The Anchor Lounge, located in the middle of the street, has a great many regulars who appear to never leave the bar, only occasionally seeing the light of day when they peer out of the front door.

Across the street is Busy Bee's, a corn dog stand with dollar beers in styrofoam cups. Next to the Anchor is a bar that is closed because it sold too often to minors. Another corn dog stand, Christy's, also sells beer in disposable cups. Around the corner is Fannies on the Beach, yet another hamburger joint that sells beer-to-go.

The video arcade seems to be the training ground of the next generation of Sixteenth Street regulars. The pillar of these establishments, Doc's Bar, is the oldest. Established in 1946, Doc's is the closest Tybee comes to having an institution. From the outside, with its plain wooden frame, the bar could have been transplanted from a Kansas border town. It is not one of the better bars in the city.

Doc's is a fisherman's bar that also caters to eccentrics. It can be a rowdy place, with a bumper pool table, dart boards, high stools affixed to a huge bar, and small tables scattered throughout—a bar where "types" can be observed. Doc's opens early and closes late. Across the street from City Hall, Spanky's Beachside draws persons who are interested in politics and anyone who is concerned about atmosphere. The DeSoto Beach Club is the island's largest bar and satisfies aging baby boomers. T & M's, much like Doc's but located at the other end of the island, offers regular patrons a choice largely based on one's point of origin. These bars are much nicer than the ones on Sixteenth Street, and the clientele is of a much more "stable" variety.

I mentioned that many "types" can be seen at Doc's and at all houses. Aaron and John were two such patrons. They gave every appearance of being drunk. Their words were slurred, their hand gestures slow and exaggerated. Seated at the same stools they normally occupied, the two friends shared their sixth pitcher of beer. It was a hot Saturday so they had arrived around 11:30 A.M. to escape the heat.

They started out by playing games of bumper pool, and the loser had to purchase the first round. Then, they proceeded to ceiling darts, a game in which participants stick a thumb tack through a dollar bill and throw it over their heads. In order to win, the dollar must stick to the ceiling. Should one bill miss and float to the floor, the other player earns the dollar. Should both dollars stick, the process repeats itself until a winner is declared.

Doc's was almost half full. Another pair had taken over the pool table and were quietly concentrating on their shots. Several other regulars studied their drinks and seemed to be fixtures at the bar, rarely moving or hardly breathing. Several fathers were assembled around some tables, having stolen away from their exasperated wives, who were watching their children scream their little heads off on the rides at the kiddies fair next door. A couple of well-worn ladies sat at one end of the bar, smoking cigarettes and talking loudly to one another. It was an average summer Saturday afternoon.

"Well, I'm sick and damn tired of working there," Aaron said, taking a slug of his beer.

"I know, I know," John replied.

Neither man said anything else, each trying to will his brain to formulate some words and communicate them to the mouth so the conversations would not drag. Aaron and John had known each other for years.

Aaron was a red-headed man of about twenty-eight years, twice divorced, and thin from lack of eating but with a small beer gut. He had worked for the railroad since high school, but had ceased learning long before his graduation.

John was a mountain of a man, bald with a brown beard that was reddened by the sun. He worked several jobs, having mastered the art of cutting meat, fixing cars, washing dishes, and driving the garbage truck. He was often heard saying that he was an upwardly mobile professional who only drank to support his habit of occasionally working.

"I'll tell you what I hate about the railroad: the hours. Shift work is a bitch. You just can't plan your days. The minute you get used to sleeping during the day, they change your shift and you got to sleep at night."

"Good thing you sleep on the job. So it doesn't really matter, does it?" John had a booming laugh that caused all of the fathers to eye him suspiciously and fearfully.

"Yeah, yeah," Aaron smiled but did not laugh.

"I thought you liked your job. What was that story you were telling me the other day?"

"Ah, about the bum I caught riding the train?"

"Yeah, that one. How did it go?"

"Well sir, I was walking the line, making sure all the connections were right, when I see this guy jump out of a box car. He was dirty and sweaty and seemed to be out of breath. I called out, 'Hey, boy! What do you think you're doing?' Well, the old fellow dropped his head 'cause he knew he had been caught, then he just told me he was tired. Can you believe that? Just tells me he's tired."

John grinned as he nodded his head.

"So I ask him why he's tired. And do you know what he tells me? He says he was hopping the train in Jacksonville and he sees this open box car. So he runs alongside of it, throws his bag inside, reaches up, and throws his self in. Except this box car ain't just empty; it ain't got no floor."

Both men were laughing.

"So the guy tells me he's so tired 'cause he has just run all the way from Jacksonville to Savannah, and he's too damn tired to care if I call the police or not. I didn't know whether to believe him or not, but it sure was a good story. I was laughing so hard that I never did see him slip away."

John roared with laughter, and again all eyes turned toward him. The group of fathers paid their bill and quickly returned to their wives.

"Did you check to see if the box car had a floor or not?" the big man asked.

"Naw, it didn't matter. It was too good a story."

"Yeah, it is."

The two men were quiet again for some time, almost giving the impression they had fallen asleep. The only evidence they were still awake was the occasional raising of the mug to their lips, a deep draw of beer, and the sound of the glass as they placed it back on the bar. When these moments of silence overcame them, the other patrons would devote full attention to their own drinks and conversation. When they talked, however, most everyone seemed to cock at least one ear in Aaron and John's direction, anticipating whatever wisdom two drunks might have to dispense.

"What we need to do is start our own business," Aaron finally blurted. "I want to be my own boss."

"Here's to being your own boss!" John announced, raising his glass into the air. The two men clinked the mugs and again drank deeply.

"I'm serious," Aaron continued, "and I been thinking about it. We need to get into the funeral business."

"The funeral business? I ain't interested in being no grave digger," John protested. His voice was loud and booming.

Last Rites and First Rights

"Not grave digging. I'm talking about burial at sea. Everybody seems to want to be buried at sea these days. Why don't we get us a boat and charge families to take their loved ones out and dump them in the ocean. The way I got it figured, the overhead would be so low, we'd be bound to make us some good money."

John was shaking his head. "Naw, I've buried someone at sea before. Last year, a guy I worked with lost his father. Anyway, this guy knows I have a boat, and he told me his father always wanted to be buried at sea. He asked if I would take him out on my boat, and I said I would. The old man had been cremated, and they had his ashes in a cigar box."

"So what happened?"

"Well, sir, his family crowds on my boat, and I take them out into the river channel. Somebody says a few words, and they go to dump the old man's ashes overboard. About that time, a gust of wind comes up and blows the ashes in the opposite direction than its being thrown."

"Then what happened?"

"Let's just say he got in my hair and up my nose, and that old man goes wherever I happen to be going."

Aaron burst into a fit of laughter. Those who overheard John's description of the funeral also sported either a smirk on their faces or shook their heads in disgust. When Aaron finally calmed down, he grew serious again.

"Well, sure there are going to be bugs to work out, and you done worked out one yourself."

"How's that?" John asked, stealing a glance at those who had overheard his experience. Everyone collectively studied their drinks as though their lives depended on it.

"We will have to be careful about sprinkling ashes at sea. I would think we would want to charge extra for that."

"You ain't kidding," John said as he washed the memory of ashes from his mouth.

"Most folks will have to be buried the old fashion way: in a casket that will sink to the bottom."

Again silence filled the bar as Aaron and John studied the possibilities. After a few moments, John took on the role of the devil's advocate.

"It won't work," he said.

"How come?"

"Think about it; bodies float. You know most every year someone drowns at the beach, and the Coast Guard spends about a thousand dollars an hour flying their helicopter up and down the beach looking for the poor son of a bitch."

"What's your point?" Aaron asked.

"They never find 'em. One of two things happens. Either the body washes up on shore, or it floats to the surface. That's what the helicopter is looking for: bodies floating on the surface."

Aaron studied on this unconsidered information for a while before telling John he had never figured on the bodies floating to the surface. His face finally lit up, and he proclaimed the solution to the problem. "We'll bury them in lead caskets. Those suckers will sink no matter how much a body wants to float."

John considered the explanation for a moment, then resumed the devil's advocate role. "Sure will increase our overhead. I imagine a lead casket costs a pretty penny. We won't make anywhere near as much."

Aaron was quick to respond. "We'll just make up the difference in our fuel costs."

"What do you mean?"

"We'll offer an economy burial at sea where we just take 'em a couple of hundred yards offshore. We won't need as much fuel and can probably do six or seven funerals in a day. For those who want the deluxe burial, we take them a couple of miles offshore, but we'll have to charge a hell of a lot more!"

Both men seemed to be satisfied with this conclusion and began to ask one another what kind of business license they would need to start the new venture. They also discussed the advertisement necessary to draw customers.

"It's going to take one hell of a pitch to draw a lot of customers," John announced.

"Why's that?" Aaron asked.

"Because all of our customers are going to be dead!"

Both men agreed they would need to hire the best public relations firm in Savannah, and they continued to speculate on the business proposal.

As it approached four o'clock, several patrons left to take a nap to prepare for serious drinking on Saturday night. Parents were collecting their children on the beach and herding them into their cars to make the drive home. Boats were backlogged at the public ramps as those who had spent the day on the water all decided to come in at the same time. As the sun began its slow descent, activity increased across the island. Only John and Aaron remained focused on the task at hand, fortifying their commitment by ordering yet another pitcher of beer.

Last Rites and First Rights

Suddenly, John spoke. "Wait a minute? If we go dropping all of these lead caskets in the water, do you know what is going to happen?"

Aaron did not seem to have a clue what might occur.

"We're going to be building artificial fishing reefs."

"What in the world has that got to do with anything?" Aaron asked.

"Well sir, you know what an artificial fishing reef is. Whenever the Department of Natural Resources wants to attract fish to an area, they find themselves an old boat or car, tie a bunch of old pipes and tires and whatever other junk they want to get rid of to it, and sink it out at sea. Because we got us a flat, sandy bottom out there, this serves as a natural attraction to fish and, bam, next thing you know we got tons of fish all gathered at one place."

Aaron stared at John with glazed eyes. "I still don't see what that's got to do with anything."

"It'll help us keep the overhead down," John explained.

"How's that?"

"We can charge the family a fee for first fishing rights! After they bury their loved ones, they can continue to visit 'em as much as they want and catch fish at the same time."

Aaron smiled and patted his partner on the back. "Johnny, I believe that you have just come up with our advertising campaign. We'll call it 'Last Rites and First Rights: Burial at Sea and Guaranteed Fishing Privileges.'"

Both men congratulated the other on having a most productive day, paid their bar tab, and carried themselves out of Doc's Bar into the hot summer sunset.

The Smell
of Politics

My wife, Janice, and I decided we would be good citizens and attend a meeting of the city council. Before the meeting, scheduled to begin at 7:30 P.M., we went to dinner at Spanky's Beachside. Spanky's caters to a young crowd, and the bar serves those residents who feel they are a higher class than the customers of the bars located on Sixteenth Street. It has a pleasant atmosphere, except during the summer months when several thousand people move freely from the beach to Spanky's and back again.

An outdoor bar was set up to serve the summer crowd, though it did not have a significant impact on the number of people who use the facilities. Summer customers drink beer in the sun, walk past the outdoor bar to the restroom, stop at the outdoor bar on their way back to the beach, and thirty minutes later the ritual begins again. In the summer Spanky's is a never-ending people festival. During the off-season it is a nice, low-key, neighborhood establishment.

The bar and restaurant are separated by a four-foot-high wall with long dinner tables on one side and small, round bar stands on the other. We sat on the restaurant side next to the dividing wall and overheard that most of the saloon's patrons were fortifying themselves for the city council meeting.

Peeking into the bar, I saw a mob of citizens crowded into every bit of available space. Most people were dressed casually, in shorts and colorful beach shirts. The men obviously did not care for socks. One or two of them wore ties, loose around the collar; none wore jackets. An array of raw vegetables, chicken fingers, chips, and dips were arranged on a table so they could easily be held in one hand while the other hand remained fixed to the drink. Everyone seemed to know one another, and the discussions were exceedingly noisy.

As we finished a good dinner, we checked our watches and saw that it was about five minutes before the scheduled meeting. We quickly paid the bill and prepared to leave. There was a backlog at the door, however, as most everyone else in the restaurant had decided to leave at the same time we did. Collectively, we poured out the door and, staying intact as a group, marched across the street to City Hall. Glancing back at Spanky's, I noticed it was virtually empty of customers.

City Hall is a plain, one-story building with an exterior of red brick and a sheet rock interior. Black and white photographs of former mayors line the hall. A slender hall leadds past offices on either side into a foyer that has two sets of double doors leading into the main meeting room. For that night's meeting, folding chairs were set up to accommodate approximately 200 people. Portraits of mayors line this room too, although more are in color. At the end of the room, the specially constructed desks of the elected official, city attorney, and city manager were arranged. Other attentive staff sat nearby, ready to provide whatever was called for in a moment's notice.

The Tybee government consists of a mayor and six council members. The mayor runs against other candidates for the same position. The council members all run against each other, and there may or may not be a slate of candidates running as a ticket. The six candidates having the top number of votes comprise the council, with the one having the largest number of votes serving as mayor pro tem. A city manager runs the government between meetings and is supported by a small, underpaid staff.

The island has a reputation for dirty politics. There is a factional system on the island, but it is not divided into parties of Democrats and Republicans. Instead, the system is dominated by the two largest families on the island. All candidates run as either "Solomons," "Hostis," or "other." The families take the place of political parties, although most everyone runs on an anti-government, no-taxes, and no-rules platform.

The heart of city campaigns has been the post office, where all residents pick up their mail. Persons running for political office, as well as those running to oppose the election of a certain individual, stop anyone exiting or entering the government building. Citizens have to run a near gauntlet of would-be officeholders just to collect their mail. After the elections, former candidates sue one another for slander as a way of keeping their names in the public's mind until the next vote.

On that night, the room was filled with laid-back citizens and even looser politicians. Were it not for the fact that the elected officials sat behind the somewhat formal, prefabricated desks with name plates signifying who they were, one would be hard-pressed to distinguish the politicians from the audience.

Short sleeve shirts, cotton pants, and no socks were definitely the order of the day. Several members of the audience held red glasses that they had carried from Spanky's, as did one member of the council. An elderly man—with his long, white hair drawn back in a ponytail—sat at one end of the council's table, sipping from his glass from time to time and trying to look presidential. I remembered seeing him in the bar, drinking what someone had referred to as "hard liquor."

The mayor—a tall, thin man with a crew cut—called the meeting to order. The minutes were approved as reviewed in the pre-council session, and a public hearing was called on a number of issues listed on the printed agenda. The first item was the purchase of a new van for the recreation department, but no one wanted to speak either for or against it. The second consideration concerned an effort by the Tybee Beautification Committee to plant trees along Butler Avenue.

Several people described how "blighted" the island's primary thoroughfare seemed to be and asked everyone to imagine how nice it would be if trees lined the road. Several of the older speakers reminded the older council members what the road used to look like before it was "paved over and four-lane." A somewhat younger speaker quoted a song from the 1960s as she described the desecration of Butler Avenue: "They paved paradise and put up a parking lot."

The councilman with the ponytail cleared his throat and spoke. "Excuse me young lady, but they did not pave paradise and put up a parking lot. They laid down a four-lane highway."

Discussion continued until the mayor announced that the matter would be referred to the business session, which, someone told us, followed the public hearings.

Upon hearing this, the man seated beside us nudged me in the rib cage and shook his head. "I don't know why they do it this way," he softly explained to us. "Seems to me it would be much easier to finish everything as it came up rather than deal with it twice."

The person sitting on the other side of us volunteered, "That's because they hope we will all go home before they ever get around to voting on anything."

The final item in the public hearing was listed on the agenda as "Dogs in a Residential Area." Some twenty people immediately lined up to address the council. The first speaker was a middle-aged woman with a round face and short, black hair. She stood behind the podium, was given a hand-held microphone, and began speaking before it was turned on. No one heard anything she was saying, and members of the audience screamed out, "Turn it on!" or "We can't hear you!" She nervously fidgeted with the microphone and turned it on, knocking it with her hand to make certain it was indeed working. A loud pop, pop, pop reverberated throughout the room. People screamed out, "Okay! For God's sake we're not deaf!"

"Mr. Mayor and distinguished leaders of Tybee Island," she read from a prepared speech, "I want to call the council's attention to a matter on Lewis Avenue where residents take great pride in the fact they live in the United States of America on an island named Tybee."

"Oh, Christ," the person sitting next to us said, "I wonder how long she worked on this?"

"We love this island," she continued, "and all of us take pride in our street. All of us except one."

"All right," our neighbor gleefully whispered, "here it comes!"

"This one neighbor is not someone who cares for his neighbors or who loves this island. While most maintain well-manicured lawns, this man never cuts his grass and has junk laying all over his yard. While most residents of Lewis Avenue are kind, decent people, this man is not even kind to animals; and it is because of these animals and the well-being of our neighborhood that we have come here tonight.

"This man has dogs in his yard. Not just one, two, or even three dogs. This man has fifteen or twenty dogs penned up in his back yard. Most appear to be hungry and are only fed occasionally. Several seem to have the mange and are in dire need of a veterinarian. If all this was not bad enough, this man has not cleaned up after his dogs in quite some time, and it smells. They do not just smell when you pass by his house; the smell permeates up and down Lewis Avenue. To put it bluntly, distinguished members of the Tybee City Council, this stinks!"

All of the persons standing in line to speak, as well as many members in the audience, burst into applause. They clapped with serious expressions on their faces, giving the impression it could just as well have been a toxic waste dump that had opened in the middle of the street. Those who did not applaud laughed. Even the mayor was grinning as he pounded the gavel to restore order in the room. Several members of the council tried to look serious by cupping their hands and covering their mouths, supposedly trying to convince everyone they were considering the speech.

The next speaker was an elderly man, wearing an old, white shirt and a black tie. He stood proud and erect at the podium, waiting for silence to return before he addressed the council. His appearance was much more dignified than anyone who held public office. When the applause and laughter finally abated, he cleared his throat and held the microphone in front of his face.

"I am also here," his baritone voice began, speaking in a slow and deliberate fashion, "in order to address the concern I have, not so much for the animals—although that is sad enough—but because my wife has serious health problems. It is not very often that she is well enough to go outside and sit in the yard where she and I have spent forty-seven years of our lives together."

The audience again applauded, but this time the manner and tone was respectful and warm. The gentleman waved his hand to several people seated nearby. The mayor offered his congratulations to such a happy marriage. Quiet anticipation again filled the room.

"As I was saying, my wife has been quite ill, and it is only on the rarest of days that she is able to come outside and sit in our yard. That is," he began rushing his words, "she *was* able to sit in the yard until that man allowed all of those dogs to take over the street. Now, the sweetness of the odor that the soft, summer, evening breeze brings to my house is overwhelmed by the mountain of dog feces next door. This man appears to be using these animals to build a tower behind his house. In the Holy Bible we read about the tower of Babel, but what this man seems to be constructing is a tower of sh . . . !"

Before the word got completely out of his mouth, the room again burst into laughter and applause. The mayor and council made no attempt to hide the amusement they had with the proceedings. There was more laughter than applause, and the man sitting next to me said that the meeting was better than anything on television. The Mayor again banged the gavel and, several moments later, the room grew quiet. The third speaker was a much younger man, wearing shorts and sandals. While obviously nervous, he also made an elegant argument.

"You all know," he commenced, "that during the months of August and September it can be awfully hot on this island. The daytime temperature can be close to a hundred degrees, and at night it is often in the high seventies or low eighties. While many have the luxury of air conditioning, many do not. I don't. We rely on open windows and ceiling fans to cool our house. Now I want each of you to imagine what a backyard full of dog feces smells like after it has cooked in the hot sun on a hot August day."

Once again the room exploded into laughter and some applause. Every member of the council was openly giggling, some laying their heads on their desks and pounding it with one of their arms. The faces of those in the assembly were red from the lack of oxygen. Only those waiting in line to speak maintained their poise, although by then I was sure it had to have become a most arduous task. Finally, and mercifully, the mayor pounded the gavel.

Several other speakers echoed the same themes. The neighborhood was beautiful, but one yard was a mess. Everyone was kind, but one man was cruel. Everyone cared for others, but one man disregarded his friends. Everyone loved animals, but this man maintained a Nazi-like concentration camp for dogs. There was no holding back the laughter, and each address was constantly interrupted.

A sense of commotion from behind demanded the attention of most people in the room. A rather aggravated young man with wild black hair and dirty blue coveralls stood motionless with folded arms and steel, gray eyes. Almost one by one, heads turned to see who was quietly requiring their notice, as the momentary silence came this time without the benefit of the mayor and his gavel. When most persons were aware of his presence, the man quickly made his way to the podium.

"I think you've heard enough from those against me," he said, although the high-strung and anxious voice did not match the bodily presence. An almost moaning quality was felt when he spoke, as though it were one of the dogs describing captivity rather than the camp commandant.

"Yes, it is true I live on Lewis Avenue, and it is true I have a lot of dogs. Most of them are strays that I have picked up. I love animals, and I care for these dogs. It is also true I have to leave them unattended for long periods of time. I work long hours, and it takes most everything I earn to get by. It's hard enough making ends meet without the dogs. But do you know how much it costs me to feed sixteen full-grown dogs every day? I brought a few receipts to show you."

He left the podium and handed the sales slips to the mayor, who passed them to the other members of the council. He slipped back to the speaker's stand and resumed his defense, while the council members studied the small pieces of paper.

"As I was saying, I love dogs. My so-called good neighbors leave them to starve or hit them with their cars, but I take them in, give them a place to stay, and feed them. I'm what you call a . . . " He hesitated, searching for the right word, ". . . a . . . humanitarian."

Several members of the audience asked themselves, "Humanitarian?" Others grasped the humor of the misplaced word and chortled to their neighbor.

"No, that's not right, I don't know what you call it, but I'm a . . . a . . . dogertarian."

Many of the persons present must have thought this was a proper word, as only a handful laughed. Some were being won over by his argument. Those standing in line groaned, and I heard a couple of "boos." The white-haired, pony-tailed council member folded his arms and nodded his head up and down. The recording secretary asked how to spell dogertarian, but no one volunteered any assistance. The mayor told her to look it up and called for the proceedings to continue. The young man, however, stated he had said everything he had come to say.

The mayor asked if the members of the council had any questions. The pony-tailed councilman stated that he had something to say, and he pulled the microphone down in front of his mouth.

"Now, I have lived in this very neighborhood for the past twenty years, and my house happens to be next door to this young man. And I want to say that, in all of those years, I ain't never smelled anything." He shoved the microphone away from his mouth, folded his arms, and leaned back in his seat. His face showed a smirk of amusement.

One of the members of the audience yelled out, "That's cause you're drunk all the damn time!"

The councilman jerked forward in his seat and snarled, "What did you say?"

"What you got in that tea glass you brought over here from Spanky's? You want to let everyone have a taste?"

"You want to step outside? I'll show you what I can do with this glass!"

The mayor banged the gavel with more vigor than he had all night. Other members of the council restrained the pony-tailed one and told him to calm down. Some members of the convention laughed, some shook their heads in disgust, and a few clapped—although no one seemed to be sure what they were applauding. It was some time before the mayor restored order to the meeting.

After conferring with the attorney, the mayor finally pronounced that the public hearing was over and the matter would be brought up during the business part of the meeting. The audience booed and hissed.

"See! What did I tell you?" my neighbor said. "Now watch, they're going to drag things out until it's too late for most of these folks to stay. Then they'll probably not do anything about issues that are important to a lot of people."

"Are all of the city council meetings like this?" I asked, not believing that such an episode as the one I had just witnessed could be common practice.

"Oh no," he said, "some are even better."

Janice and I left at 10:30 P.M. before the dog incident came to a vote. It was a warm, pleasant night, and we held hands as we walked beside the paradise that had been four-laned. Neither of us spoke until we were almost home.

"Do you think it's like that all of the time?" she asked.

I told her I didn't know; and we walked on in silence, enjoying the beauty of the summer night, the full moon overhead, and the sound of the ocean's ever-present background noise. When we reached our house, we wrapped our arms around one another and enjoyed the moment.

"I learned one thing tonight," I said, breaking the silence.

"What's that?" Janice asked.

We took a few steps towards our home, and I answered while we walked. "If the television set ever goes out, there's plenty of free entertainment on this island. That guy was right. Tybee politics are better than anything on television." We both laughed and went to bed.

The Senator's Wife's Orchid

W hen Jim walked into his former brother-in-law's apartment, he knew the shape Marcus would be in. Even though it was 2:30 in the afternoon, the room was dark with all of the shades pulled shut. As always, the place was a mess with empty beer cans scattered beside the overstuffed, brown easy chair positioned in front of the television set. Next to the chair was a card table filled with overflowing ashtrays, magazines, and half-empty coffee cups. He had obviously spent another night in the bars on Sixteenth Street and was likely paying for it this morning. Jim hated it when he didn't have any choices.

Jim was a well-dressed, slightly overweight, successful, real estate agent. Most of the homes he sold were on Skidaway Island, a private resort community that had been developed in several phases and attracted snowbirds from the north. Over 4,000 homes had been built and sold since the late 1970s. As a result, Jim had experienced a radical change in lifestyle.

He was formerly a struggling salesman, forging a decent middle-class lifestyle. Because he was one of the first agents to market the Landings, and because of family spread all over the country who marketed for him, he had made a small fortune off the commissions of hundreds of newly constructed homes. Now he owned a fashionable home in the Landings, drove a vintage red Corvette, and had friends in some very high places. In spite of these changes, he remained a good ol' boy who liked to have a good time. He worked hard at developing a polished image, and it paid off. When he was not working, however, he played as hard as he worked.

"Marcus! You here?" he called into the darkness.

"Yeah," came the harsh, muffled reply. "Bathroom."

Jim flipped on the lights and saw that the apartment wasn't as bad as he first thought. Aside from the cluttered card table and the empty beer cans, everything else was more or less clean. He recalled his own early bachelor days and was glad he was now married to Cindy.

The daughter of a state senator, who did not particularly care for his son-in-law, Cindy brought a sense of class into Jim's life that had eluded his background. She was educated at the University of Manhattan; he had attended the University of Georgia. She played the piano, spoke French, and was on the wish list of every board of directors in Savannah. He fished, hunted, and drank beer with his buddies—of which Marcus was one.

Marcus was the brother of Jim's ex-wife, who was now married to a homebuilder. Marcus and Jim remained friends throughout the divorce and saw each other every few weeks. During those times, Jim would offer Marcus a temporary job, ask to go fishing, or simply need a companion on a business trip. Jim hated to travel alone, and Marcus provided companionship when Cindy could not go. But more important to him, after spending a hard day working, Jim wanted someone to unwind with. Sometimes he wanted Marcus to go and Cindy to remain home. He sometimes worked hard at putting on airs for her, too.

Walking into the bathroom, Jim saw Marcus hunched over the vanity, lining up a white powder with a razor blade. Delicately he brushed the powder into a long, thin line.

"What in God's name are you doing?" Jim demanded.

"Got a bad headache, Bo. Give me just a second, and I'll be with you." With this explanation, Marcus rolled up a dollar bill and snorted the substance first up one nostril and then the other. Once he had inhaled it, he coughed and cleaned his throat.

"I can't believe you have anything to do with that stuff," Jim said in an indignant manner.

"What?" Marcus seemed genuinely surprised. "Can't somebody take an aspirin anymore?"

"An aspirin? You just did a line of cocaine!"

Marcus roared with laughter. He was a large man, well over six feet and weighing 252 pounds, and could crush most anyone. Bald with a beard turned red from the ocean sun, he loved to laugh and did so often.

"Cocaine? This ain't nothing but headache powder. I told you that I had a headache."

Jim looked at the blue and white BC powder wrapper in Marcus's hand. Sure enough, Marcus had just snorted two aspirin up his nose.

The Senator's Wife's Orchid

"Why in God's name didn't you just swallow it like you're supposed to?" Jim asked.

"I don't know," Marcus led him down the hall to the living room. "Seems stupid for all that medicine to go to my stomach when the pain is in my head. It just seems logical to put the medicine where the suffering is located."

If Jim had wanted to argue with the logic, he knew from experience there was no use in engaging his former brother-in-law, so he let it pass. Entering the living room, the contrast in the two friends would had been apparent to anyone who saw them. At least, Jim had the image of success.

He had married right, had money in the bank, and could afford to take trips most anytime he wanted. Most of the junkets he took were, in fact, escapist in nature and had nothing to do with business, though he often implied that they did. His expeditions had become fabled to his friends, as Jim and his designated comrades—including Marcus—would fly the Senator's six-seat private plane to the Bahamas to fish, to Atlanta for a Braves game, or to any number of places Jim chose.

Marcus, on the other hand, was a beach bum. The rent on Tybee was still cheap and reasonable. He worked as a meat cutter, mechanic, and garbage collector—just enough to pay the rent and buy gas for his home-made fourteen-foot boat. He had purchased the boat from a child education specialist who gave up his former life and became a shark fisherman on the island. If the boat's motor was broken, or if he was between jobs and could not afford fuel, Marcus would simply walk the beach or hang around Doc's Bar.

Marcus's claim to fame on the island was the fact that he was the clean-up hitter for the Tybee Market softball team. Marcus would drink beer before, during, and after the game; but he hit at least one homerun over the center fielder's head almost every game. He also loved children, helped senior citizens, and would quit any job if he thought he could help a friend. Everyone on Tybee loved Marcus.

"So, what's up?" Marcus asked as he searched for his well-worn deck shoes with holes in the tops.

"I promised I would go to the Bahamas with the in-laws to play some golf, and we need a foursome. You want to go?"

"Where in the Bahamas?" Marcus asked, although Jim could tell by the tone in his voice that he would accompany them.

"Flying into Marsh Harbor in the morning at eight, staying in Hopetown on Saturday, and playing golf in Freeport Sunday morning. You'll be home Sunday night."

Marcus thought Hopetown was the most gorgeous place on Planet Earth. It had views that photographers made into postcards, diminutive white Cape Cod houses on small narrow streets, and no cars. Everyone there owned a boat rather than a car, because when they traveled they went to another island and not into town. Jim knew it was Marcus's translation of heaven.

"All I got to do is fly over there with 'em, play one round of golf, and fly back after the game?" Marcus asked, slipping on the newly-found shoes.

"That's all."

"What time we leaving?"

"Meet me at the aviation field at 7:30. The plane leaves at 8:00. The Senator is flying us down, so we won't have to talk to them. The old lady will sit up front with him."

"You buying the beer?" Marcus asked, obviously wanting to get as much out of the trip as he possibly could.

Jim grinned, took his former brother-in-law's hand, and began to shake it. "I'll buy the beer."

On the following morning, Jim waited nervously at the front door of the air station hoping Marcus would arrive in time. He also knew the Senator would demand they find a fourth player "down there" and leave promptly at 8:00. He knew that it could be a hour's drive to the airport from Tybee. If he had not left early enough, Marcus might be caught in traffic, cursing and speeding as fast as he could between traffic lights. While Tybee was still relatively free of congestion, the other islands linking it to Savannah were often congested with automobiles by 7:30 A.M. The price of rapid development is a road system that cannot keep pace. At 7:45 Marcus's old Ranger pickup truck screeched to a halt.

"Come on," Jim commanded, and the two ran through the terminal to the airfield. The Senator's wife was already behind the cockpit. The old man greeted Marcus with a stiff formality, threw the bags into the storage cavity in the wings, motioned them into the plane, and precisely at eight o'clock the plane took off. Settling into the seats beside one another so they could stretch their legs, Marcus fell promptly asleep. Jim stared out the window, praying it would be a good trip to the Abacos Islands at the top of the Bahamas.

The Senator's Wife's Orchid

An air pocket jolted the plane and awoke Marcus by throwing him upwards. Jim was glad because Marcus had been snoring and now, hopefully, it would be his turn to get some sleep. Marcus reached into the small cooler he had brought on board and at 9:30 opened his third beer of the day. He drank the first two beers a few minutes after midnight, but he had quit early so that he could get up and drive to the airport at the crack of dawn.

As he looked out the window, Marcus saw that the plane was over the crystal clear ocean. The water was so pristine that he could see shipwrecks resting silently on the bottom, near the coral reefs that had been their demise. He began humming a Jimmy Buffett tune, thinking of the words while searching for more sunken dreams.

> Yes I am a pirate
> Two hundred years too late
> The cannons don't thunder
> There is nothing to plunder
> I'm an over-forty victim of fate
> Arriving too late
> Arriving too late[1]

This was his favorite song and, high above the Caribbean Sea, he began to wonder about Tybee.

Tybee was a small town by the sea, but he could sense the development coming. In the past ten years a thousand new families had come to call the island their year-round home. It was still pleasant enough from September until May, but during the summer months the island was kidnapped by thousands of tourists each day.

The Tybee city council was inundated with requests from developers to build condominiums and, sooner or later, Marcus knew they would sell the island to the highest bidders. Perhaps it was time for him to consider moving on. Hopetown would be the place. He knew that in the next few years he would need to give the move serious consideration; playing pirate on Tybee was increasingly difficult.

Suddenly, the plane rolled over, and Marsh Harbor lay underneath them. The small air strip appeared in front of the plane. The Senator guided the plan down without any assistance from the air traffic controller, who did not have the capacity to talk to pilots while they landed. Obviously, only experienced aviators could land at Marsh Harbor. Marcus finished his beer and prepared to begin the weekend with the Senator and his wife.

While the Senator did not care for Marcus, he loved golf and was willing to be associated with most anyone as long as a game was involved. There are almost as many golf courses as there are people in Savannah, and he had mastered most of them, preferring now to play in different places. His business and political leadership took place on the greens. His marriage would have likely been troubled if his wife had not picked up the game and was perfectly willing to putt instead of shop or pay attention to their daughter's dates.

The Senator and his wife were horrified when Cindy announced her engagement to Jim and spent several hours trying to talk some sense into her head before taking off for a golfing tour of Ireland. The wedding plans were made through a series of overseas telephone calls, and the family was reunited thirty minutes after the wedding rehearsal was underway.

Cindy's parents had learned to actually like their son-in-law, although love was probably out of the question. Jim obviously cared for their daughter and had a handicap of seven. He was also willing to travel with them on short notice to play golf, likely because he wanted to win them over and be included as a full-fledged member of the family. Jim cared much more about what the Senator might be able to do for him; the Senator only saw Jim as a rather convenient partner on the course. Apathy best described how the Senator felt about him.

Jim's mother-in-law was another story. She pretended they were all one big, happy family. She always greeted Jim with a peck on both checks and let him in on little secrets to keep his wife happy. Through five years he had learned that these minor revelations were nothing more than one of the ways she tried to manipulate what he and his wife did, who they associated with, and almost every other facet of their lives. Jim had learned to play her little games, as Cindy called her mother's activity, but she was little more than the thorn on the rose he had married.

After everyone disembarked, Marcus patted the pilot on the back. "Hell of a job, Senator! I was looking out the window, and there was ocean, and then there were pine trees, and then there was this here airstrip—which ain't but about ten feet long from the air, but I see it's just long enough to land a six-seater."

The Senator's wife grimaced and made a face. Jim shut his eyes tight and wondered if he should have spent a bit of time explaining Marcus before they actually met him. All he had said was that his former brother-in-law had helped him through the divorce with his first wife. He left out the fact that the two of them stayed drunk for approximately three weeks.

When he opened his eyes, the Senator had launched into a lecture of how difficult it is to land without radio contact on such a small airstrip. He and Marcus were walking into the customs office in the tiny one-story airport. Marcus was patting the Senator on the back with one hand and holding his fourth beer of the day in the other. His mother-in-law watched them for a moment before turning her attention to Jim.

"Where did you say you found him?" she asked, before turning and following her husband.

No one had bothered to carry his or her luggage except Marcus, who had brought only a tote bag stuffed with whatever he had packed and his golf clubs. Jim found a lone cart near another plane, loaded his family's bags, and pushed it to the custom's office. The Senator and his wife were already on the other side of the yellow line, waiting for their bags to be inspected.

Marcus, still holding onto the beer, was being frisked by a customs officer wearing a crisp khaki uniform. Jim sighed and began to have serious doubts about his judgment. After a few moments and a serious inspection of Marcus's bags, their passports were stamped, and, noticing that the Senator and his wife had already gone, they caught a cab to the docks.

"You got to watch yourself, Marcus," Jim said when they were on their way.

"Why's that?"

"Well," Jim explained as he opened his first beer of the day, "my in-laws are eccentric people."

"I know, high class know-it-alls!" Marcus opened another beer. "Your father-in-law gave me the whole history of American aviation."

"Well, he is a smart man. His job demands that he know a lot."

"I know. He's a politician, which means he ain't a normal human being."

Jim retreated into silence for the rest of the trip, knowing there was no point in arguing. Five minutes later they were at the docks, where the Senator had rented a boat to take them to Hopetown. Marcus wanted to drive, but Jim reminded him this was the Senator's trip so, after loading the luggage, they took a seat in the back by the cooler. The Senator skillfully steered the boat out of the harbor across the channel to Man o' War Cay because his wife wanted to stop at Asbury's Sail Shop and purchase a bag. Marcus announced that he would like a nickel bag himself.

"Oh, they're cheap," she told Marcus, "but certainly not that cheap." Marcus looked at Jim as though to say, "I told you they're not normal."

For years Mrs. Asbury, her daughter, and her granddaughters have been sewing canvas bags, hats, jackets, and purses at the small shop above the slip where the Senator docked. She greeted the Senator and his wife by name and offered them a piece of cake and some iced tea. The small wooden shop had items for sale hanging over the walls and on two shelves. One corner was devoted to old sewing machines, where two girls worked while Mrs. Asbury fussed over the Senator's wife. Jim and Marcus thought all the bags looked the same, so they walked across the narrow street to a block wall that protected someone's yard.

"What you think of this place?" Jim asked.

"It's every bit as pretty as Hopetown," Marcus replied, staring up and down the streets. "God, I love it down here. I wish I could pick Tybee up and lay it in this water."

"No you don't," Jim responded.

"Uh? Why not?"

"Once I was here with Cindy. She was wearing a string bikini, and when we walked into Mrs. Asbury's shop, you would have thought the devil himself came in the door. Seems as though this is a very prim and proper place. 'Showing of the flesh,' she called it. They wouldn't even serve us until she put a shirt on. Tybee just wouldn't fit in these waters."

Marcus said he guessed that Jim was right and retreated to the boat where he drank beer until the Senator and his wife finished shopping. Looking into the clear water of the harbor channel, he saw giant red starfish the size of a baseball glove laying on the bottom. He wanted to grab his snorkel and dive down for a look, but thought better of it.

Tybee is the perfect island for these waters, he thought, regardless of what Jim might say. The people on his island would loosen up these folks. His musings turned to the brownish-green marsh waters of the Georgia coast compared to the crystal clear water of the Bahamas. They were both beautiful in their own way.

While staring at a starfish, Marcus wondered where the dolphins were. There were always pods of dolphins near Tybee. Sharks, too, were plentiful in the river channels. He had not seen any in the Bahamas. There was simply more life, big and small, off Tybee; and the more life, the more success a fisherman will have.

The Senator's Wife's Orchid

The Senator and his wife returned with a bagful of canvas totes, wondering why Mrs. Asbury refused to take the American Express card. They commented about how much better it was than the other credit cards. Marcus thought it would be nice to have any kind of credit card; it did not matter which kind.

As they entered the channel and headed for Hopetown, Marcus silently drank another beer and wondered what was happening at Doc's Bar back home. In Hopetown, the Senator and his wife announced that they were meeting friends for dinner. Jim and Marcus would have the night to themselves. Things were looking up.

After checking out their accommodations, Jim and Marcus took the boat back to Marsh Harbor and had dinner on the veranda at Wally's, where they ate fried pork chops stuffed with cheese. Tourists and regulars crowded the porch, and the owner greeted them all. He welcomed each to the "finest restaurant in the Abacos" and told them to enjoy.

When they had finished supper, the two friends walked down the street to a duty-free jewelry shop where Jim purchased for Cindy a silver bracelet of dolphins grabbing one another by the tail. With the family business behind him, Jim found Marcus hitting the bars. First, they settled into a harbor bar, drank pitchers of beer, and listened to a reggae musician play beach music for the tourists who had come by boat.

At midnight, when the performer packed away his guitar and ordered a beer, they caught a cab to the island's interior to a local road house that is popular with islanders. As the only white people in the bar, they commanded immediate attention. As the only Americans, they were expected to buy a round for everyone, which they gladly did. In return, they were invited to play pool and shoot darts. Marcus said he believed this was the Bahamas version of Doc's Bar. At three o'clock, they returned to the docks and steered into the darkness of the river channel.

Navigating by the stars, they discovered it was too dark to be island hopping in waters only vaguely familiar to them. Going slow, the normal fifteen-minute trip took more than an hour because a cloud cover blocked out whatever light the stars provided. The wind also picked up, and the rain started.

As they approached the lights of Hopetown, Jim instructed Marcus to stand on the bow and tell him when they were close to the docks. Marcus held onto a rope as the boat rocked into the harbor, peering through the rain and trying to see the docks. Jim steered in what he thought to be the right direction. He had been to the islands several times, but had never approached them at night. Besides, he was tired and drunk. He wished he could feel the safety of his bed.

"Whoa!" Marcus's voice screamed, startling Jim. He immediately pulled back on the power, but it was too late. The boat slammed into the piling and knocked Marcus into the passenger's seat next to Jim.

"I guess we made it," he said after he realized he was alright.

"Yeah," Jim replied as he wondered about what damage the boat had incurred, "God watches over fools and drunks."

"You know, you've got to love a God who does that, his friend commented."

They stumbled to their quarters and slept until 2:30 the following afternoon. Marcus woke first, snorted a headache powder, and walked outside to the pool where he dove in and felt life return to his body.

The Senator and his wife were sunning beside the pool, drinking some tropical fruit drinks and looking repulsively at one of their foursome. Jim dove into the pool ten minutes later, and the two friends floated in the cool water until they felt like talking. After saying good morning to everyone, Marcus ordered his first beer of the day from the bar.

The rest of the day was a repetition of Friday night. The Senator and his wife went somewhere, and the two friends returned to Wally's—where they ate broiled grouper—and then to the Road House, where their new best friends were waiting for them. Every time they prepared to leave, someone challenged them to another game of pool. Then someone broke out the cards, and they played poker until 4:30 A.M. Again they steered through the darkness to Harbortown, and at 5:30 they were sound asleep.

At 6:30 the Senator was pounding on their door and yelling that they had to leave in ten minutes if they were going to make tee time at the course. Jim bolted out of bed and began throwing his possessions into his suitcase. Marcus moved slowly, putting on the same clothes he had worn since leaving Tybee, and picked up his tote bag. Both felt terrible and were still under the influence of the night, which showed no signs of wearing off. Marcus wanted a beer, but the cooler was empty, and it was early Sunday morning.

The boat ride across the channel was worse than anything the two had ever experienced. The water was choppy, and each time the bow slammed against a wave, their heads seemed to explode. The Senator and his wife were furious with their son-in-law and his friend and refused to say anything to them. Marcus would swear the old man was trying to hit each and every wave.

The cab ride was bumpy, too. Jim and Marcus held their heads between their hands and tried to refrain from throwing up all over the back seat. On the plane ride to Freeport, the roar of the engine echoed in their heads, and both seemed to lose their hearing. The early morning jaunt from one end of the Abacos to the other did little more than confirm a suspicion that they had died and gone to hell.

Because of the Senator's determination, however, they teed off promptly at eight o'clock. It was apparent that anger and talent abounded in equal proportions on the course and the game would be a quiet one without the usual bantering that accompanies a friendly game of golf. Jim worried that his in-laws would never speak to him again. He did not want to think of how they would relate the experience to Cindy. Marcus seemed to be trying so hard to concentrate on hitting the ball that he was oblivious to anyone around him. Both had the strange feeling they were living a nightmare, and they sliced the ball into the rough.

By the second hole, Marcus told Jim he really needed a beer to settle his stomach. Jim agreed, but it was early Sunday morning, and there wasn't a soul on the course they could bribe to go get a six-pack. By the third hole, Marcus could stand it no longer. He reached into his golf bag, pulled out a bag of pot, and quickly twisted a joint.

"You can't do that in front of them!" Jim excitedly whispered.

"It's a simple case of self-preservation," he replied. "Either they're going to kill us, or I'm going to die anyway. I'd rather choose the way."

By the fifth hole, both men were sharing the joints and feeling better about things. Their game actually improved, too. No longer slicing into the rough, they began to hit the ball true and straight and played below par. The Senator and his wife were too angry to be in top form, unable to relax, and unwilling to concentrate. The scores drew even.

At the ninth hole, the Senator's wife sliced the ball into a thicket. Disgusted, she stormed into the woods to retrieve it. Jim and Marcus stayed on the end of the green opposite the Senator, continuing to share the smoke. They were feeling much better but did not want to invite the further ire of the Senator and his wife, who seemed more frustrated about their higher scores than how high Jim and Marcus were.

A golf cart wandered onto the fairway, and the three men turned and watched it approach. Two persons from the maintenance crew had finally arrived for work and were immediately dispatched to inspect the greens after play had already begun.

As he rolled to a stop on the green, one crewman's eyes lit up, and he called out to Jim and Marcus. "Hello, mon. Did not know it would be so soon that I would see you again," he called in the sing/song Carribean voice.

Jim and Marcus recognized one of the fellows from the Road House where they had spent the past two nights. Marcus walked over and pumped the hand of one of his newest best friends and whispered into his ear. Laughing, the man reached into the back of the cart and pulled out Marcus's first beer of the day. After taking a long drink, he threw another beer to Jim. The Senator observed them and was offended, but neither Jim nor Marcus seemed to care. After a few moments, he stormed over to the newly-developing party.

"Go in there and find her!" he commanded.

Dutifully, Jim and Marcus left their laughing friends and proceeded into the thicket and called for the Senator's wife. They heard her in the distance and hurried over, fearing she may be in trouble. They found her standing under oak trees, admiring some of the largest flowers they had ever seen.

"Aren't they beautiful?" she gleefully explained. "I've got to have one."

"Nice flowers," Marcus said.

"They are orchids," she explained as she tenderly stroked the petals. "All orchid blossoms have an irregular shape and are made up of three sepals and three petals, each with beautiful colors. One of the petals, called the lip, always has a unique shape. The early Spaniards found orchids in the Bahamas and thought they looked like the holy dove that flew down at the baptism of Christ. They called it the Holy Ghost flower. That's what these are. They don't grow in America."

Plucking one of the flowers, she happily escorted Jim and Marcus back to the golf course and showed the blossom to the Senator. While he did not share her enthusiasm, he had been married long enough to know when to fake it, so he spoke glowingly of its beauty. Marcus and Jim obtained another beer from their friends in the golf cart. The game resumed after several minutes, and the Senator's wife asked the others to hold the flower while she hit the ball.

At the seventeenth hole, several other course employees joined the ensemble as observers. They had also brought more beer, and each shot was loudly cheered. The Senator's focus was on winning the game, especially since an audience was in tow and he hated to lose, particularly to drunks.

The Senator's Wife's Orchid

The Senator's wife's interest in the game was compromised by her concern for keeping the orchid intact until she could safely secure it in the plane for the trip home.

Jim was concentrating on the game, hoping it would earn his in-laws' forgiveness and little would be said to Cindy. For Marcus, the game was little more than an excuse to drink beer and have a good time. He lagged behind the others, choosing instead to enjoy his newest best friends. The only ones who fully appreciated the entire scene were the employees who would have another great story to tell about those crazy Americans.

At the eighteenth hole, the scores of Jim and the Senator were tied, while Marcus was one stroke behind. Because of her attention to the orchid, the Senator's wife's score had escalated, so she was no longer a factor in the game. Jim teed off first and hit the ball straight and true. Obviously, he would be on the green after the second shot. The Senator's wife gingerly handed the flower to Jim and hit a lazy high ball that fell twenty-five yards shy of his. She retrieved the orchid before the ball even landed.

The Senator's ball curved as it flew down the fairway, landing just out of the rough. Marcus placed his beer on the ground and carefully studied the ball, the fairway, and the club. He shifted his weight from one leg to the other, bent his knees twice, and hit the ball so hard everyone knew it would carry for a major distance. It landed just shy of the green.

The Senator cursed, but no one heard because of the loud cheering of the islanders. Smiling, Marcus gave several high-fives and received congratulations with a good-natured humor. Jim and the Senator and his wife picked up their bags and began walking toward their next shots. Marcus jumped into one of the carts and was triumphantly carried to the green where he opened another beer and waited for the others to finish their shots.

Jim hit; his ball landed just ahead of Marcus's. The Senator's wife took her time securing the orchid before finally hitting another high, lazy ball that was still well short of the others. The Senator hit a good corrective shot that landed several yards behind Jim's. Cheering and praise greeted Marcus's approach to the ball. Again placing the beer at his feet, he repeated the shifting of his weight and the bending of his knees. He hit the ball, and the force carried it straight to the marker. Bouncing on the green, the ball slowed to a roll and fell into the cup. He had hit an eagle on the hole. The applause and cheering erupted, and again Marcus high-fived his fans. The Senator rolled his eyes in disbelief.

Still in hopes of obtaining forgiveness, Jim purposely hit his next shot too hard, and it rolled to the far side of the green. The Senator followed. His ball landed fifteen feet from the cup. Again Jim hit the ball too hard, and it rolled past the hole. The Senator hit again and just missed the hole. After a last purposely-misplaced shot by Jim, the Senator's ball fell, and he claimed sole possession of second place. The cheering and noise followed them back to the clubhouse where the Senator rushed everyone into a waiting cab enroute to the airport.

In the back of the plane, Marcus pulled two beers out of his pockets and handed one to Jim. "Here's to another day in paradise!" he said, clanking his can against his former brother-in-law's.

The Senator and his wife did not speak until they approached Miami, where he ordered everyone to fill out the declaration cards necessary to pass through customs. By his signature, Jim declared the bracelet to be all that he he was taking into the United States. Likewise, Marcus scribbled his name on the bottom of the card and handed it back to the Senator. Upon landing, the Senator led them into customs where a line had formed. Taking their places at the end, each quietly waited for his or her turn.

Progress was slow. Jim tried to fix his eyes on something of interest, but the office was bland; there was nothing to entertain him, so he kept his eyes straight ahead. He absently began to read the declarations on a sign that hung over the officer's desk: "It is unlawful to bring in certain amounts of liquor, clothing, and jewelry unless duties are paid. It is unlawful to bring drugs into the United States. It is unlawful to enter the country with a pass-port other than your own. It is unlawful to bring plants not indigenous to the United States."

Jim froze and wondered about his mother-in-law's orchid. His eyes met hers. She pulled him close and quietly said in her fake, happy, everything-is-going-to-be-fine voice, "Jim, I hope you don't mind. I put my flower in your golf bag."

Fear shot through his body. What was the penalty for attempting to smuggle an illegal orchid into the United States? What would his in-laws say if he refused to help them? What would Cindy do when she heard that her husband was arrested in customs? What would the cost of bail be for such a thing? Would the Senator pay it? A thousand things ran through his mind. Suddenly, they were at the front of the line. The Senator and his wife were opening their bags and joking with the officer. He turned to Marcus in panic.

The Senator's Wife's Orchid

"Marcus," he said in a rush, "she put that damn orchid in my golf bag!"

Calm and seemingly unconcerned, Marcus asked, "So?"

"SO!" Jim almost shouted. "It's against the law to bring flowers into the country. I'm going to be arrested."

"Naw," Marcus coolly answered, "I wouldn't worry about it."

"What do you mean you wouldn't worry about it?!"

Marcus smiled, put his arm around his former brother-in-law, and said, "I put my pot in her golf bag."

Note

[1] "A Pirate Looks at 40," *AIA* (MCA Records, 1974) compact disk.

Running with the Dolphins

The pea green porridge color of southern seawater may surprise and even offend first time visitors to the Atlantic barrier isles. Why the murky water? Especially in summer, the ocean here is laden with diatoms. These microscopic, one-celled plants ("phytoplankton") whose populations explode in warming water. Their chlorophyll-rich bodies give the sea a greenish tint. The brownish color is caused by abundant detritus (decayed plants and animals) floating in from lee side salt marshes. Current-borne silt from rivers emptying into nearby estuaries also muddies the mix . . . a stirring of the ocean, the land and living and dead sea life which forms a nutritious but colorful nature soup. Blue seas are beautiful to view, but in fact they are quite empty of ocean life.[1]

—Todd Ballantine
Tideland Treasure

The sand is gray, the sky is gray, and the ocean is a muddy brownish-gray. The clouds are hanging very low over the beach, and it is difficult to see five feet in front of my face. Jogging in such weather is testimony to my belief that it is easier to stay in shape than it is to get into shape.

I began running when we moved to Tybee because there were few other athletic options. The small island does not lend itself to health clubs or racquetball courts. The few tennis and basketball courts on the island are normally overtaken by teenagers, so I run a couple of miles most everyday when I get home from work.

My wife told me I was crazy for jogging on such a dreary afternoon, but I do not trust myself to let a day or two pass without the run so, in spite of her chastisement, I found myself outside. Half a mile into my run, I wondered if I had made a poor decision. I was soaking wet from the heavy mist hanging in the air. I knew the ocean was to my left. I could hear the waves crashing and imagined how the ocean would look if I could see.

White caps would cover the brown-green sea like whipped cream. From the sky, it would appear to be an endless cup of hot chocolate, which would have tasted pretty good at that point. Having found shelter of their own somewhere, no pelicans or sea gulls would be seen, and the animals of the sea would be near the bottom far away from the churning surface. To my right were the houses of Tybee filled with warm, dry, and comfortable people who knew better than to go outside.

My wife was probably right, so I decided to shorten the run and return home. I was guessing at the distance because I could not see any of the familiar landmarks. Usually I will run to the north end, somewhere around Fort Screven, or to the southend jetty. Because I live in the very middle of the island, it is more or less equal distance whichever way I go.

Normally, I begin my run against the wind, laboriously pumping my legs against the unseen but very much felt obstacle. At either end of the island, where the wind rushes unencumbered across the ocean surface and picks up speed as it sweeps onto land, it takes every bit of energy I have to make progress. At the halfway point I turn and, with the wind at my back, pick up speed and run faster than I am really capable until I arrive home. This is quite a workout if a northeastern wind is blowing from the fall until April.

From May until November, the runs are easy but hot. The humidity or the temperature may slow my progress as I suck in air and forget about my legs, causing the sweat to pour from my body. There is no wind during the first leg of the run, but halfway I reverse the routine because of the wind. Beginning with the wind, I quickly break a sweat and at the halfway point can hardly breathe. Turning around, the gentle ocean breeze blows in my face, and I am able to catch my wind and jog home.

The only strategy on that day, however, was to see where I was going. There was the constant danger of stepping into an eddy or tripping across a tree that had washed ashore. Concentrating on placing one foot in front of the other, I simply thought about the run. "Hurry up and finish," I told myself. "This is one rotten day."

Then we almost ran into one another. I assume he could see no better than I. His head was down, and he didn't seem to be paying attention to where he was going. I was the one who broke my pace and jumped out of the way. Neither one of us could have seen the other coming. One second I saw only the gray fog, and the next moment he was in front of me. He had long, brown hair and a long, flowing beard and wore faded red pants and no shirt. After jumping out of the way, I stopped and turned to meet the person who was just as crazy as I for running on such a day. Upon turning, however, I caught a brief glimpse of his backside as he disappeared into the soupy day. After waiting a moment, all I could do was continue the run until I was inside my warm and cozy home.

I did not give this episode another thought until several weeks later when I was basking in the warm clear sunshine, well-oiled with suntan lotion and sitting on the beach. My youngest daughter, Chelsea, played in the surf. The ocean was calm and clear, more green than brown. Pelicans flew in their V-shaped formation overhead. The sea gulls circled in search of people eating so they could land nearby and assume the beggar's position, waiting for the scraps. Because it was Saturday, I had already run and planned on devoting the remainder of the afternoon to my daughter and the ocean and that evening to my wife and our deck.

Janice had returned to the house to shower and—I suspect—take a nap so she could stay up late, listen to soft music, and watch the stars that seemed incredibly bright in the black night. I watched Chelsea playing in the water with her dolls, conducting an imaginary conversation as she bathed them in salt water. I recall thinking that spring is the best time of the year and there is no better place to live than Tybee.

Most people who live on Tybee enjoy the ocean in one of three ways. Those who own boats normally fish. Actually, this is an understatement. Fishing is the central focus of their lives. These folks will quit their jobs if they think it is a good day for fishing. Some persons, such as those at The Breakfast Club, fashion their occupations so they have ample time to fish. Barry would arrive at work before the crack of dawn, work until one o'clock—unless it was a good day for fishing, in which case he would close early—clean up as quickly as possible, and then take the boat out to fish.

Of course, one doesn't need a boat to fish. Surf fishers are in abundance on the island. At the south jetty, people who do not own boats gather and fish from shore. They bring coolers, chairs, and tubes that they shove into the wet sand. They cast their lines, sticking their rods and reels into the shafts of the plastic. In this way they have several lines cast at one time.

Some persons cast their nets, holding one piece of the mesh in their mouths while grabbing other parts in both hands. Twisting their bodies, they hurl the net into the water, let it sink, then draw the string to catch the fish into the net. Net casters appear to like solitude and find some place where they can be alone. Fishermen and women make up the largest minority population on Tybee.

Some residents own boats but do not fish. They usually purchase a power boat, jet ski, or sailboat. They can afford to take time from work and spend long periods of time playing with their toys on the water or entertaining. These are typically people from Savannah who launch their boats from the public ramp at Lazaretto Creek or rent slip space at one of the island marinas.

Other residents such as myself simply take their chairs, coolers, and books to the beach and choose a spot to sit for several hours where they watch their children, the ocean, people strolling the shoreline, or anything else that may grab their attention. For whatever reason we do not own boats, and we fish only on occasion—if at all.

Everyone who sits on the beach wants a boat for traveling to the unspoiled, uncrowded, and uninhabited beaches of Little Tybee or Ossabaw Island. The boat will have to wait, but I do not mind. Most Americans cannot leave their houses, take a very short walk, and sit beside the ocean. I was content sitting there, watching the sights of a warm spring day at the beach.

I was sitting at the high water mark at low tide. In this way, I could easily keep an eye on Chelsea and also watch those persons who ambled beside the water. Most people walk directly beside the ocean when strolling down the beach because they do not wish to get wet but want to be as close to the ocean as possible. As I watch them, I saw him.

The long, brown hair was thick and stringy. The beard was halfway down his chest. The faded red shorts were obviously old and fit loosely on his thin frame. He did not look like most runners, who have a vigorous appearance, but had a lackluster way about him. He ran at a fast pace, however, moving very quickly in front of me. Then he grew smaller as he made his way down the beach. Looking like a strung-out old hippie, he seemed very out of place jogging beside the ocean. I wondered who he was and why he ran. He clearly wasn't a jock.

Over the course of the summer, I saw him on a regular basis as I ran or sat in my chair. He always ran as though he was distracted. Every few steps, he would turn his head toward the ocean and back again in a most unorthodox style. He was obviously in shape. I became fascinated with him. Who was he? What was his route? Why did he steal glances at the ocean with every few steps?

Running with the Dolphins

Runners rarely speak to one another. In fact, most of them ignore others. Now and then a few will wave at persons they pass. Only the closest of friends attempt to carry on a conversation. Whenever we passed one another on the beach, I waved, but he seemed to ignore me. I wondered if he was one of those runners who was into spirituality and concentrated on heavenly matters, punishing their bodies like Martin Luther did as he formulated the groundwork for the Reformation.

I was certainly not obsessed with him, just merely curious. For weeks I would not see him, and he would not enter my mind. Looking back, I suppose I should have taken this to mean he did not live on Tybee. The island is quite small—only two-and-a-half by one-half miles with 3,000 year-round residents—so I am certain I would have seen him somewhere if he lived here. He was simply another one of the oddities one encounters when living on an island.

One day Larry called and asked if I would like to sneak away and go fishing. Larry was the director of the Red Cross in Savannah, lived on Wilmington Island, had his own boat, and was hooked on fishing.

"Come on," Larry told me, "work is never that important. Meet me at the Lazaretto Creek ramp in one hour, and we'll catch some fish."

"I can't," I replied. "I promised my wife I would be home by noon so we could spend some quality time together."

"I don't care if she comes," he answered.

I waited a few moments, hesitating and not knowing what to do.

"Come on," he provoked me, "it is a glorious day, and the fish are biting."

"Let me call her, and I'll call you right back."

I had been deep sea fishing only once in my life and wanted to do it again. My wife said she would like to go. I immediately terminated the conversation with Janice and called Larry's office.

"All right," I said, "we'll meet you at ten o'clock."

I then told the rest of my co-workers that I was feeling bad and drove home as quickly as possible. Throwing my work clothes into the floor, I waited for my wife to arrive. When she finally arrived home, I rushed her. I was as excited as a little boy on Christmas morning. I could not wait to get offshore again.

My first experience of deep sea fishing was with my son, father, brother, and Scott—a childhood friend so close to the family that we refer to him as our illegitimate brother. I was living in Louisville, and we were home for several weeks during the summer. Knowing how much I loved the sea from a distance, my Dad chartered a boat, and we spent a day fourteen miles offshore fishing for king mackerel and Spanish mackerel. It was a glorious experience. I caught the largest fish, a king weighing seventeen pounds.

At one point during the expedition, when the boat was still on a sea of glass, we decided to take a swim. Climbing into the crow's nest, where the captain navigated the craft twenty feet above the deck, we dove into crystal clear water. Offshore, away from the influence of the marshes, the ocean is green and crystalline. The bottom was forty feet down, and we could see jellyfish floating ten and twenty feet underneath. We watched one another go down and then return to the surface. My memories were of a marvelous day. I wanted to live it again.

When Janice was finally ready, we sped to the designated place. Larry already had his twenty-four-foot whaler in the water. After introducing him to Janice, we followed the Lazaretto Creek, past the little lighthouse into the ocean. It was another perfect day. Following the channel markers, Larry made his way to the Texas Tower, eight miles offshore.

"This is where we will fish." he told us. "It's illegal to tie up to the tower, but I don't think any police cars will be riding by, so let's catch some fish."

Janice had never been offshore before. From a small town in West Georgia, she was experienced at pond fishing, especially for catfish, but this was a brave new world. She felt fine on the twenty-minute ride to the tower, but the moment we stopped the problems began. Larry and I tied the boat to the tower, baited the hooks, and dropped our line. Janice turned green. We had no sooner settled back than she spoke.

"Guys, I can't stand this. I guess it is the smell of the gasoline and the rocking motion of the boat."

Larry and I turned our attention from the lines to her. She was seasick but tried her best not to show it. She said things were fine so long as the boat was moving, but that she would not be able to stand this particular spot.

Larry was gracious enough. He said it was no problem, released the lines, and in no time at all we were moving toward the open sea. When we stopped, Janice was certain she was sick and suggested she jump into the ocean in hopes it would pass.

"Besides," she said, "I have to go to the bathroom."

Most people do not understand that only very expensive boats have heads, or bathrooms. Larry's skiff was costly enough, but there was no head.

Running with the Dolphins

"No problem," he said while pointing at the ocean. Janice understood and jumped into the cool ocean water. When she climbed back aboard the vessel, she looked as green as the water.

"I hate to do this," she began, "but I can't stand it. You are going to have to take me back. I'm going to be very sick if I stay out here."

I couldn't believe it. We were eight miles offshore and had not even begun to fish, and Janice was ready to go home. Larry was kind enough and steered the boat toward the coast. Noting the look of disappointment on our faces, she added, "Just drop me off and you two can fish."

As a husband, I interpreted this to mean she really felt bad about being sick and ruining the day, but needed us to make certain she got home as quickly as possible. I also felt she probably wanted me to go home with her. As a fisherman, however, Larry viewed this as a golden opportunity. Instead of heading back to the boat ramp, he changed course and veered directly toward the beach. A hundred yards offshore, he announced she could go home and that we would take her up on the gracious offer to continue fishing.

"How deep is it?" Janice asked.

"I don't know, but this is as close as I can get. I don't want to tear up the motor by dragging it along the bottom."

Janice looked at him, then at me, and then back to Larry. I was worried she would be mad at me for quite some time if I didn't go with her. Larry continued to tell her it would be fine.

Hesitating, she jumped out of the boat and stood in chest-deep water. "Have a good time," she called, wading to the beach. We watched until she stood on the shore and waved. Then Larry gunned the engine, and we headed out to the open sea. I felt bad about dumping Janice, but Larry said she would come around once we caught a bunch of fish.

We went out to the L-buoy, tied up, and dropped our line. Immediately we began to pull in black bass. One after another, we hauled them in almost as soon as our hooks sank below the surface. As we pulled them in, Larry became excited and stood up in the bow of the boat and screamed toward the heavens, "Wooooooo!! I love it!!"

After we ran out of bait, Larry cut up one of the bass and used it to allure fish to bite the hook. We continued to pull them in at a quick pace. When we finished three hours later, ninety-seven fish were in the cooler. Larry pronounced it a good day.

We returned to Lazaretto Creek, and I followed Larry to his house where we cleaned the fish. Splitting them equally, he explained that black bass are a great fish to eat. "They taste like a freshwater catch and can be cooked in a number of ways. I like to just fry them in a light batter."

Thanking him for the day, I packed my trunk with the filets to make the twelve-mile trip from Larry's house on Wilmington Island to Tybee. In spite of Janice getting sick, it had been a very good day. I played a Jimmy Buffett tape and prepared to enjoy the ride through the marshes, over the Lazaretto Creek bridge with its magnificent view of the ocean, and through Tybee Island to my house where I would dazzle my family with the catch.

On the side of the road he stood, thumb pointing in the general direction of Tybee, and wearing the faded red shorts. The long hair and beard blew in the breeze left as cars passed him. I pulled my car over, and he climbed in. With yellowish, gaunt fingers, he clutched a rolled-up shirt in his hand and mumbled thanks.

"I see you run on Tybee."

"Yeah," he replied without offering anything else.

"Me, too. I run most everyday."

He did not respond. I drove in silence, trying to think of a way to begin a conversation. Each attempt was met with a simple nod or shrug of the shoulders, but no words. After crossing the Lazaretto Creek bridge, I asked where he wanted me to let him off.

"Next to Jesus," he said.

I found his statement to be quite humorous and knew exactly what he meant. One of the residents of Tybee is a very religious fellow who also constructs and paints signs for a living. He has two billboards in his front yard. One side greets all visitors to the island. Pictured against a blue background is Jesus, with white hair and a white beard, wearing a red cloak and gold crown, and holding a sword in his right hand. He is riding a horse descending from the clouds, a black cape fluttering in the wind. Twelve beams of light protrude from his backside in every direction.

To the right of the picture, written in red, are the words "Coming Soon." Underneath, in bold white letters, is the name "JESUS CHRIST." Below is the warning, "Ready? or Not." In very fine lettering, the source of the scene is listed as Revelation 1:1.

> The revelation of Jesus Christ, which God gave him to show his servants what must now take place. He made it known by sending his angel to John.

Running with the Dolphins

I stopped the car beside the sign. "Why do you come all the way to Tybee to run?" I asked before he opened the door, though I really didn't expect an answer.

Surprising me, he turned and spoke in soft, hushed tones. "I like to run with the dolphins."

"What? Run with the dolphins?" I had no idea what he was talking about.

He settled in his seat for a moment and closed his eyes while speaking. "Sometimes, when it's low tide and the ocean is as slick as glass, I'll run just at the water's end. They are always there, but you can't always see them. I'll be running, and then they surface. If you adjust your pace, you can run with the dolphins all the way down the beach. That's why I run out here."

With that he thanked me and jumped out of the car and began walking the back streets toward the north part of the island. He evidently began his jog at one end of the beach and proceeded to the other. I continued my ride home.

Atlantic bottle-nose dolphins are common to the southeast coast of the United States. This steel-colored species may be seven to twelve feet in length and may weigh up to 500 pounds. With a loud *whoosh,* they hastily inhale air through their blowholes, then submerge their melon-shaped heads. As streamlined as a missile, dolphins cruise the waters looking for squid, fish, and crabs, streaking at twenty to forty miles per hour after their prey.[2]

Dolphins are easily spotted from the shore by beachcombers when the fin breaks the surface. Tourists often mistake them for another kind of fish and scream, "Shark!" to the top of their lungs, causing a minor panic for persons who are visiting the ocean for the first time or those who have seen the movie *JAWS* one too many times.

For regular visitors to the sea or those who live on islands such as Tybee, the sight of dolphin pods—a group of four or five swimming together—is a very common sight. Comfortable with the number of swimmers invading their home, dolphins will dart nearby. They are fond of following boats and surfacing at almost arm's length. Occasionally, one will wash up on shore with large chucks of the body having been ripped off by sharks. Dolphins are very common sights on Tybee, so I failed to understand this man's captivation with running beside them.

That night, over an exquisite supper of fried sea bass, I told Janice about the rider and his reason for running. She had seen him before but did not seem particularly interested. We never had a chance to discuss it anyway, as the phone rang off the hook with friends calling to either congratulate or reprimand me for throwing my wife overboard to fish!

Apparently as soon as I left Larry's house, he called virtually all of our mutual friends and gave them a fisherman's version of what had happened. According to Larry, I badgered him to take me fishing but could not get my wife to stay at home. Once at sea, Janice began to complain and say that she was sick of fishing. Larry then said, "Look, either she goes, or I'm taking you both in so I can fish!" Given that option, I threw Janice overboard while we were several miles from shore. The story grew with each person who called. I quickly forgot about the runner.

Several days later, I had a very bad time at work. Everything that could go wrong did. I was unable to accomplish much. At every turn some crisis demanded my immediate attention. On top of that, the air conditioner went out at the office, and my suit was soaked with sweat.

The drive from Savannah to Tybee can be very therapeutic on such days. It only takes a couple of minutes to get out of the city via President Street Extension, then past an industrial district, to Whitemarsh Island, to Talahi Island, to Wilmington, and then the seven-mile ride on the causeway through the marshes. By the time I reached the Lazaretto Creek bridge, I felt that an invisible door was closing behind me and the city was left to its own devices until I returned.

Still tense when I got home, I decided to run. Running allows my body to release the stress and tension from the workday. A couple of miles later, I am relaxed enough to have an intelligent conversation with my wife, ask my children how their days were, and begin planning supper.

I changed into my running shorts—interestingly enough manufactured by some company that named them "Dolphins"—put on an old football jersey, and donned my running shoes. I am not one of those runners who makes a fashion statement whenever he jogs. I do not wear anything remotely similar to spandex and never consciously determine whether I am color coordinated or not.

I do not like to run with anyone. I like to set my own pace without having to worry about keeping up or, worse, waiting for someone to maintain my pace. I do not care to have a conversation while I run; I prefer to think about whatever enters my head. I do not keep my time, as some runners do, or have an established course. The only agenda is to run until I feel like stopping. I have found running as a conclusion to my job is a very effective way to separate my work life from my home life.

On this day, I ran north on Butler Avenue, Tybee's main street. It was a hot day with no breeze. The asphalt was blistering, the humidity high, and my pace slow. Eventually, I made the wide turn at the north end of the island and proceeded to the post office, turned right, and jogged to Memorial Park and the baseball field.

I passed the nursing home and entered a new, but not completed, subdivision named Captain's Row. The streets are paved and the lots marked, but there are only a couple of actual houses. I went to the end of the imaginary neighborhood and turned into the sand dunes. The sand held onto my feet as I labored to reach the top and, once there, saw the beauty of the Atlantic Ocean spread out before me. Turning right, I ran down the beach.

I felt healthy and quickened my pace. Each ounce of sweat brought out the frustrations of the day. It felt good to be home. There were few people on the beach. Only an occasional couple would pass me—holding hands, talking, and looking for seashells. The other runners seemed to have chosen to stay on the streets or not run at all because of the ninety-degree temperature. My steps naturally carried me toward the water, where there were no waves—only the soothing lapping of the sea against the shore.

Everything was so still and motionless that I could easily pick them up. Three or four dolphins swam in the same direction I was running. They were near the shore and easily made their way, gliding through the calm waters. They would submerge, travel a distance, and then surface and blow a puff of air from their holes. It seemed as nothing else existed except for the dolphins, the ocean, the sand, and my steps. My pace matched their speed, and together we made our way down the beach.

We were so close I could see their eyes when they surfaced. Dark and delightful, they appeared to hold the dreams of everyone who has ever sailed the seas and know all of the mysteries of the deep. While I knew that the natural curve of their mouths form an upward turn at either end, it seemed they were smiling at me. I felt invigorated. I ran and they swam. I pushed myself to a runner's euphoria while they effortlessly rolled their bodies through the surf.

The south end jetties were in sight. With time running out, I continued to steal glances toward the sea. I was almost at the stopping point; I could not climb the rocks that formed the bulkhead and keep pace. The dolphins would continue into the open sea, and I would have to turn away from them at the jetty. I did not want this experience to come to such an abrupt end.

Ten feet from the jetty, I slowed to a halt, and the dolphins submerged. I cursed and gazed toward the water. Then one dolphin jumped straight up, reaching for the sky and bringing its body completely out of the water. It seemed to be suspended in the air and twisted its torso and flipped. Its head entered the water through the same hole it had created when it jumped out of the water. The rest of the pod surfaced again, blowing the air through their holes and making the loud *whoosh* sound. Then they were gone.

For several minutes I stood gawking at the sea. The words of my runner friend came to me: "I like to run with the dolphins." I knew what he meant and understood why he hitched a ride to Tybee every day just to jog. It made perfect sense.

I have tried to explain the experience to others, but they merely think it was "cute" that I saw dolphins while I was running. They either claim it must have been nice or describe the last time they saw dolphins. These

Sunrise on Tybee Island

experiences frustrate me, and I no longer attempt to share what it's like to run with the dolphins.

I take solace in an episode in the life of Ernest Hemingway, as described by Arnold Samuelson. Once when sailing his boat, *Pilar*, from Key West to Cuba, he found himself in an enormous school of porpoise that he estimated to be a mile long and four miles wide. Steering the *Pilar* with the porpoise for over an hour, whole smaller schools at times jumped in unison in the almost-purple water. After watching for some time, Hemingway told the others on board not to try and write about what he had seen in a serious way: "Things like this are almost impossible to describe."[3] Sometimes, however, the image has become so much a part of who you are that you cannot help but try.

I still see my friend from time to time. While we do not speak or wave, he seems to have noticed a difference in me. Ever so briefly, he turns his head my way and looks into my eyes. Ever so slightly, a smile graces his lips.

Notes

[1] (Columbia SC: University of South Carolina Press, 1991) 8.

[2] Ibid., 202, 203.

[3] *With Hemingway* (New York: Holt, Rinehart, Winston, 1984) 90-94.

DeSoto Slam Dancing

Love of live music is apparent on Tybee. Unlike other parts of the country where artificial muzak—computer-generated sound systems and over dubs—are played "Live! on tape," real musicians playing authentic instruments are part of the night life on the island. Second only to public intoxication in popularity, special musical activities take place throughout the year.

On the Fourth of July, several bands usually perform at Spanky's Beachside, drawing a younger crowd where the songs are loud and what one hears may or may not have any resemblance to real music. There is no question, however, that it is live. Several bands play at the Tybee marina on the deck above the oyster beds. They are always good, leaving the crowd wanting more. Ron Dennin, who has a very faithful following of locals, has played at the Outback Cafe for what seems like several decades.

The biggest musical extravaganza is the annual Beach Music Festival where famous shag bands from the fifties and sixties—if the members are still alive and able to walk—play on the strand to the delight of hundreds of aging baby boomers. The Swinging Medallions, the Tams, the "original" Tams, and probably the not-so-original Tams have all played the festival. The event has always lost money, but it is so popular no one dares to cancel it for fear of riots.

The absolute center of Tybee's musical world is the DeSoto Beach Motel. In the island's early glory days, when the train was the sole connection to Savannah, the ornate DeSoto Hotel was built. According to photographs from that era and the oral history of the island's older residents, it was extremely popular and catered to the cream of South Georgia society. It burned after the road was built but came out of the ashes like a phoenix in its latest form. The current facade is a mere shadow of the original and—

while it's not much of a hotel—the dance floor is adequate and the bands are normally good.

The DeSoto caters to aging baby boomers by making certain the bands know shag tunes and beach music or can at least play the greatest hits of the sixties and seventies. The best band that plays at the hotel is Ansel, Strong, and Braun.

Butch Ansel and Jay Strong have been playing together for almost twenty years and have perfected the art of knowing what a beach audience likes. Several musicians have been added to and subtracted from the duo, one configuration of which recorded an original song, "Rachel," and has its own cult following. Denny Braun is the real musician in the trio, playing every instrument imaginable, including the moog synthesizer. The three men never fail to draw a crowd, support the waitresses, and work the crowds into a dancing frenzy so they order beer when the music stops. A better band has never played on Tybee.

In no way does the DeSoto try be anything other than what it is: a beach bar. Customers are invited to enter barefoot, wet, in their bathing suits, or just about any other way imaginable. Apparently the ownership is trying to upgrade the building because people always seem to be working on the facade, although it never seems to look any better. Several years ago the bar was modified to accommodate more customers. Only one person seemed to notice, however. His stool had been moved, causing him to crash to the floor when he tried to sit and bruise a thigh. Fortunately for the DeSoto, he doesn't recall the incident.

The outside thatched hut bar at the DeSoto has a very large deck facing the pool on one side, the ocean on another, and the inside bar from the rear. Savannah Steve plays live at the outside bar, dressing like a white boy doing an impersonation of a Jamaican on Halloween. His music also impersonates the sounds of the Beach Boys and some Carolina shag bands.

Savannah Steve is a big hit with the drunken crowd and has written two original tunes, "Moon over Tybee" and "Tybee Island Girls," the latter of which is sung to the tune of "California Girls." Many customers claim that listening to Savannah Steve on the deck of the DeSoto is as close to heaven as is possible on earth. Of course, they are drunk when they say this.

On Sunday nights during the summer, the DeSoto sponsors a talent show. Beginning at nine o'clock, Ron Dennin and his band play a few tunes to warm up the crowd. Several judges, always tourists, are chosen to evaluate the proficiency of the "acts" and are paid in free drinks for the duration of the show. Typically, the first few acts are regulars who sing songs or tell jokes, while members of the audience are given ample time to sign up for a performance.

The end result is "The Gong Show Goes to the Beach." If an act is bad, the drunken audience heckles or boos it off the stage. Islanders know what to expect, but some very talented tourists have been known to rush crying from the stage, pack their luggage without delay, and change their vacation plans to Hilton Head. Tybee has never been known for its tact.

Second perhaps to the annual Beach Music Festival, the DeSoto talent show is the singular most popular happening on the island. Hundreds will begin arriving as early as four o'clock to secure a good seat for the nine o'clock show. This is one of the few occasions where islanders willingly mix with tourists and Savannah residents. The show is simply too good to squabble over what constitutes class on Tybee. On some nights, fans have been so numerous they have climbed onto rooftops to see. It is fortuitous that the talent show season is only scheduled July through Labor Day.

The appeal of the talent show is hard to explain. It is certainly not the talent, although some is quite good. Broadway numbers, impersonations, folk music, and gospel hymns have all catapulted individuals to fifteen seconds of fame. The atmosphere offers little. The stage is much smaller than the bar, seating is limited, and the sound is drowned by the ocean. In all likelihood, collective drunkenness of the audience is the foundation of the success. On the other hand, it could be that the greatest number of performers are tourists, and this is merely another of the island's way of paying them back for choosing Tybee over Hilton Head.

One Saturday night Janice told me that Ansel, Strong, and Braun were playing at the DeSoto. After dinner, we fixed our drinks (islanders always fix the first drink at home as a way of staying within the family budget) and found good seats near the dance floor. The DeSoto was already crowded, which we knew would pump up the band. By the end of the first set the bar was wild, filled with exhausted dancers drowning their thirst, middle-aged women lining up outside the ladies room to fix their immaculately teased hair, and younger women going to the men's restroom because the line for the ladies room was too long. Knowing it would be a wild night, Janice and I decided to listen to the second set and leave.

The band began with beach music, and the Tybee Island Shag Club—a mix of senior citizens and lesbians—dominated the dance floor. This group did the Bus Stop, a choreographed step with dips and turns, and the jitterbug, but abandoned the floor when a slow song was played. When the band began playing Little Feat's "Dixie Chicken," a crowd favorite, the place went wild. It seemed as though everyone rushed away from the bar and jammed onto the dance floor. Janice and I opted to guard our seats rather than risk dancing.

As I watched the crowd, I was struck by the diversity of the dancers. Older couples, who had been patrons for decades and were familiar with one another's moves, were graceful in their gestures. The lovers—who may or may not have been together when the morning started—shuffled their feet in a slow, passionate embrace that would probably be broken with the rise of the morning sun. The tourists were well dressed in newly-purchased Tybee shirts and stared in bewilderment at the crowds as they swung their arms but otherwise did not move. The drunks moved wildly about the floor, stepping in front of others and appearing to be doing some pre-mortal dance to Apollo, the god of war and lust.

One couple in particular seemed to have lost all semblance of twentieth-century humanity. He wore skin-tight black jeans and a Pink Floyd shirt with the sleeves cut off, and a tattoo was on his right arm. She had long blond hair, wore a cotton mini-dress with flower designs on it, and was the true object of desire for everyone who slow danced with a woman who had teased hair. This couple was obviously annoying the others as they attempted to carry on a conversation while throwing themselves around in wild abandon on the floor.

As the song was nearing its end, the man stopped dancing, screamed something no one could possibly hear, and decked the pretty girl with an upper cut of his right tattooed arm. The dancers ceased their gyrations, and the band stopped playing. No one did anything. The man stormed to the bar, grabbed his beer, and walked outside. Once he was gone, several people stooped down and cared for the woman. Ansel announced that the band would take a short break. The woman gradually sat up and asked what had happened.

"Honey, that son-of-a-bitch you were dancing with just knocked the shit out of you," explained a forty-year-old woman with teased hair.

She nodded but did not say anything; instead she rubbed her jaw and blinked back tears.

"What happened, honey?" the big-haired lady asked as she pulled out a pink handerchief and offered it to the young woman.

Before the woman could answer, the Tybee Island Police Department arrived with sirens screaming and blue lights flashing. Several of Tybee's finest were ready to restore calm in the midst of crisis.

"Cut the music off," one demanded.

"It already is off, you fool," Ansel said.

"Oh," replied the officer, "that's good."

"Okay," he asked everyone in the room, "what happened?"

The big-haired lady assumed the role of spokesperson. "Some son-of-a-bitch hit her, detective."

"Who?"

Everyone on the dance floor spontaneously pointed at the tattooed man who had returned to the bar and was quietly nursing his beer, trying hard not to be noticed. The entire Tybee Island Police Department approached the suspect and began an investigation.

"Did you hit her?" they asked.

"Not me," he replied.

"Okay, well everyone keep it down in here," the officer announced as the well-trained unit prepared to leave.

Unfortunately for the tattooed one, at that moment the young girl jumped up, dashed to her lover, and began to proclaim his innocence. "He didn't mean it," she pleaded. "We were having an argument, and he kind of got carried away. Please don't arrest him!" She cried and clutched onto him.

Confused, the Tybee Island Police Department caucused in a corner to discuss this new development. After a few moments, the lead officer again approached the suspect and asked, "So, you did hit her?"

"No, I didn't," he replied while taking a sip of his beer.

"He didn't mean it," she added, crying and continuing to clutch her lover.

Again confused, the police officers gathered in a corner to discuss the strange case. A regular patron of the DeSoto purchased a round for the officers, but they were on duty so only a couple took him up on it.

Again they approached the suspect: "She says you hit her."

He looked at the girl and said, "Shut up."

"He didn't mean it you son-of-a-bitch!" she said to the officer, kicking him between the legs.

Six of Tybee Island's finest immediately grabbed the two and hauled them off to the police vehicles where the blue lights were still flashing. Two of the officers had gone with the person who provided drinks and may or may not have been aware of the most recent development. Regardless, the two lovers were taken to jail.

The moment they were gone, virtually every man in the bar seemed to wake up and began demanding to know what was going on. "Did he hit her?" one asked.

After every woman in the place nodded that he had, in fact, hit her, the men offered their services. "I wish I had seen it," the man said, "I'd killed that S.O.B. for hitting a woman!"

One of the big-haired women threw her arms around her hero and said that she knew he would have. It was a shame he had been concentrating on his dance moves and missed the whole thing.

Ansel and the band began playing again, and the crowd settled down. The big-haired women again lined up outside the ladies room, and the young girls went to the men's room. Janice and I decided it was time to leave. Walking to our car, we ran into a good friend who was a regular patron of the DeSoto.

"Anything happening tonight?" she asked. We quickly recounted the episode. "Oh," she calmly replied, "DeSoto Slam Dancing. It happens every once in a while."

Chucking It

The lighthouse stands high on the other side of the marsh with its bright illumination safely guiding ships into the Savannah River channel on the one side and reminding the rest of Tybee it is home to the tower on the other. A small, thin line of trees seems to separate the irradiate column from the marsh. The small stretch of land on this side of the marsh is considered part of Tybee, but because it is isolated—connected only by the causeway uniting the mainland with the island—it is also quite different. The tiny peninsula is large enough to be home to three stages of Tybee development.

Spanish Hammock, an upscale subdivision with large wooden houses overlooking vast marshes, is home to attorneys and other well-to-do's who make the daily commute to Savannah. In town they seek to make their marks on the world and then, at the end of a long nine-to-five day, retreat to the solitude of "their" island. A recent development, it rapidly filled with the upper crust of other communities and is the first true victory of the developers and speculators who will eventually turn the island into a strip of elaborate homes that only the wealthy can enjoy. Spanish Hammock is the first glimpse of what Tybee will eventually become.

To the east of Spanish Hammock, in the middle of the peninsula, is Chimney Creek Fish Camp with its deep water slips, road house bar, and the Crab Shack Restaurant— "where the elite eat in bare feet." Surrounding the fish camp is a moss-covered trailer park that is home to the die-hard beach bums, those much too snobby to ever actually visit the beach. While the trailers are rusted and worn and would likely collapse if someone tried to move them, they are considerably homely and in various stages of disrepair. The boats in the slip, however, are well-kept and maintained to skipper at a moment's notice. Because their boats are almost parked beside the trailer doors, if The Weather Channel says so, residents will dash outside and be on their way to the open sea. Because most residents of the fish camp work—and the term is used loosely—only to support their fishing habits, islanders call the area "Criminal Creek," as some have resorted to smuggling as a viable occupation in the twentieth century. Chimney Creek represents Tybee as it was.

On the eastern side of the peninsula is Pelican Drive, a modest subdivision with a clear view of the lighthouse towering over the marshes. Representing Tybee as it still is in the present, Pelican Drive has older but well-kept homes, each with a window cocked toward the marshes or the sea. Here and there, new elaborate homes have recently been constructed for persons unable to find property in Spanish Hammock. The majority of the residents of Pelican Drive work for low wages. Many are employed by the City of Tybee as manual laborers, garbage and maintenance workers who made this secluded area their home—a safe refuge from the tourists, bars, and elected officials who live on the other side of Tybee. Here, their backs are still turned to Savannah and the rest of civilization while keeping a watchful eye on the small city under the lighthouse where they have spent the day fixing, repairing, and cleaning.

The Department of Public Works building is located beside the Tybee Water Works behind Fort Screven. It is central command for the lower tier of city employees, who gather around eight in the morning and—if they are not hung over from the night—either immediately begin their assignments or play cards. The D.P.W. is both a labor pool and a constant card game. All of the workers fit the stereotype of common laborers who have hooked onto a low-paying, steady job and carry out their projects as one might expect. For the most part, they are quite loyal and dependable and do the things necessary to maintain the island's small town atmosphere. They cut most of the grass, clean the majority of the streets, and repair the crumbling sewer system as best they are able. The City of Tybee would be unable to operate without them. Chances are that few of them will ever have any real opportunity for promotion or successful competition for other jobs—except one.

Daniel is a large, muscular man more than six-feet-tall, with thinning black hair, thick glasses, and a mean glare that has caused many people to back away as if a confrontation were a possibility. I first met him at The Breakfast Club, where he normally arrives as the first shift is leaving and before the second shift of regulars has arrived. He is obviously friends with Jordy, the owner, and Barry, the managing waiter. They speak in cordial language but scarcely say much more than greetings. He sometimes watches others at the counter with his intimidating stare, but rarely speaks. The conspicuous D.P.W. green uniform marks him as one of the city staff restricted to the grunt work of keeping the island's grass from growing too high or the plumbing from collapsing altogether. Something about Daniel is different from those with whom he works. I initially concluded that he was a likely suspect for mass murder.

On occasion his wife came with him. A pretty, small, friendly woman, Jenny—Jen to her friends—is very articulate and has a broad vocabulary. Engaging all persons around her, she participated in surrounding conversations while Daniel ordered his waffle and glared at those around him. She certainly wasn't the spouse of the typical D.P.W. worker. Over the next few weeks, I learned she worked as the Vice President for International Affairs at the Savannah College of Art and Design, recruiting students from around the world. She and Daniel had a daughter, Lisa, who was a student at the college. Jenny and Lisa seemed to be highly educated and upwardly mobile women intent on success. Daniel, on the other hand, seemed perfectly content to work for the D.P.W. While Jen read the paper over her morning coffee. Daniel focused on his breakfast and ignored the news.

A few weeks later, I was at lunch in one of Savannah's trendy restaurants and noticed Daniel seated with Lisa. Not wearing the green D.P.W. work shirt but white jeans and a black shirt, he shot me that glare; our eyes met briefly. He returned all of his attention to his daughter, who was a younger version of her mother—quite pretty and obviously intelligent, based on the snippets of conversation I overheard. Daniel and I didn't speak that day; I was far too intimidated by him, but it was hard not to wonder about him. He didn't seem to fit with the outward appearances of the rest of his family. Lisa appeared to be a normal American college student; Daniel resembled a prisoner out on parole.

As I became more of an early morning fixture at The Breakfast Club, I encountered Daniel numerous times. He kept his distance from most of the others, directing the majority of his conversation toward Barry. Once, when I was on a boat ride with Barry and Bill (another cook at The Breakfast Club), I decided to learn what I could.

"Tell me about Dan," I asked as we followed a school of dolphins through the marsh rivers.

"Oh, Dan's cool," Barry replied, taking a sip of his beer.

"No doubt about that," Bill added.

It is not that I do not trust their ability to provide an objective point of view, but Barry is a refugee from Chicago, and Bill is from Texas where the truth never gets in the way of a good story. The dolphins continued to lead us through the marsh river, diving under the boat and demanding most of Barry's attention. There was little chance of getting much information from Barry and Bill under those circumstances, but I continued the inquiry.

"What makes him cool?"

"He added the porch on our trailer," Bill explained. "The trailer might blow away, but the porch will be there until the twenty-second century. Dan does good work."

Their trailer was a small, olive green and rust, prefabricated home that had seen its better days. The inside looked like it was home to two bachelors who spent their mornings working and their afternoons in the boat. About the only homey touch was several pages ripped out of a coloring book my daughter had given them. Carefully wrapped in plastic, these ripped-out pages are the only art they own. Affixed to the trailer was an elaborate and well-built screened porch. The porch was certainly worth more than the trailer. Dan seemingly did good work on it, but comparing it to the trailer was not a proper measurement.

"What else makes him cool?" I prodded.

"Shark fishing," they both said at the same time.

"What?"

"Yeah," Barry said in his soft Chicago, southern-influenced accent. "Dan works to support his shark fishing. He's good at it."

Of the many fishermen on Tybee, this was the first time I had ever heard of one who had dedicated himself to sharks. Everyone knows there are sharks in the river channels, as they can be seen swimming in the waves at dusk sometimes, but no one goes out to catch them on purpose. Most people are scared to death of sharks, hearing the theme from the movie *Jaws* running through their minds when they swim in the ocean.

"What does he do with them?"

"Cuts them loose," Barry answered. "He won't kill them anymore. He just likes to pull them up beside the boat and look them in the eye as if to say 'I won, you slimy monster!' then he cuts them loose."

"About the only time he keeps one," added Bill, " is when he takes someone out who wants it."

"What got him into shark fishing?"

"He says life has been pretty boring since Vietnam, except for the rush he gets from shark fishing."

"He was in Vietnam?"

"Yeah," said Barry, "he was a second lieutenant and got a lot of medals for doing stuff over there. Says men felt safe around him."

I could easily imagine wanting Dan on my side if I were in a war. His intimidating glare probably was the deciding factor in several battles.

"How did you meet him?"

"He just came into The Club one day," Barry stated, "and was about to give up fishing. I hate to see it when that happens to somebody. It is so sad when someone just gives up the joys of fishing. Anyway, he hadn't caught anything for a while, and Dan wasn't used to Tybee waters, so we spent a lot of time in the boat together. He switched over to shark fishing by himself."

"He made this boat," Bill said as he pounded the bow.

"Made it?" I asked, no longer feeling as secure as I did a second ago. I wasn't sure why I thought a manufactured vessel could possibly be safer than a homemade one.

"Yeah, he made it himself and sold it to us. He gave us a really good deal. Dan is always doing that kind of stuff."

"He likes kids, too," Barry said. "If some kids want to go fishing, Dan always takes them."

I had a hard time imagining Dan liking kids. His bodily presence seemed to contradict it. It would have been easier to believe he had them for breakfast every morning. When I shared this with Barry and Bill, they told me I had it all wrong.

"No, Dan spent most of his life working with retarded and handicapped children. He's worked with kids in prison, run a group home for juvenile delinquents, and run a janitorial service with a handicapped crew."

"He doesn't look the part," I remarked.

"Oh, there's a lot about Dan that doesn't look the part," Barry revealed. "Once, he had this one kid, Cleo. The social workers said Cleo was so retarded that the boy would never be able to even ride a bicycle. Dan taught him how to drive a tractor. Cleo took the tractor on a seventeen-mile trip to make some kind of delivery. Dan says he still talks about it all these years later."

"Another time," Bill continued, "he took a group of retarded kids shopping after the social workers told him they couldn't interact publicly. Dan gave them each a dollar and told them to go buy something. They all went out and bought light bulbs, pencils, and other nickel and dime stuff. Dan proved these kids could do stuff if someone would just treat them like normal human beings."

"That's amazing!" I responded.

"Yeah, Dan's cool."

"Tell me about Jenny," I asked.

"She's pretty cool, too, and smart," Bill explained.

"Dan's pretty smart, too," Barry added.

"But in a different kind of way."

"Dan's people-smart."

"Jen is too, but she reads a lot and stuff," Bill added.

"Dan reads a lot, too."

"He does?" I asked. Dan did not strike me as the type who read books.

"Oh man, he reads all kinds of stuff. Philosophy, history . . . all kinds of books."

We grew silent as the dolphins turned and began to swim to the open sea. The sun was bright and hot, and we were all beginning to turn lobster-red as we baked on the water. Barry started the engine and said it was time to go back to Criminal Creek as he skillfully began steering the boat toward home.

"Why isn't he a social worker anymore?" I asked.

"Didn't believe in paperwork," Barry said, although I could tell he was more interested in getting back to the trailer for his afternoon nap than he was in talking.

"What's that mean?" I pressed.

"He threw it all away. Dan believes the best thing you can do is treat kids as human beings, and everything else doesn't matter."

We glided through the brown water, and I stared at the mud banks that are the foundation of the marshes. I could hardly believe that a social worker who had obviously been successful, albeit in an unorthodox way, with kids now worked for the D.P.W. I wondered what had brought him to Tybee and why the downward social spiral. When we arrived at Criminal Creek, I thanked Barry and Bill for another glorious time and went home.

Dan and Jen were at The Breakfast Club the next morning, seated in a booth with two well-groomed men in expensive business suits. Eavesdropping on their conversation, it became apparent the two were trying to hire Jen. An art college in New York was opening a school in Savannah to compete with the enormous success of the Savannah College of Art and

Design. I learned that Jen had resigned from her job and was now the wife of a D.P.W. employee who obviously did not want to return to work.

The men became exasperated as Jen explained she simply wasn't interested, even though it was a great career opportunity. They demanded to at least know the reason she would not consider their proposal. Jen said they wouldn't understand, which further frustrated them. They continued to press her for a reason until finally she agreed to tell them.

"I'd have to wear pantyhose again," she explained.

Both men looked at each other and said they did not understand.

"I said you wouldn't understand."

Everyone at the counter, who had been listening to their conversation, erupted into laughter. Dan traded his glare for a smile; and Jen, obviously proud of her rationale, giggled with the rest of us. The two men thanked her and quickly left. Moving from the booth, Dan and Jen took two empty stools at the counter. We congratulated them for sticking to their beach-bum roots and continued to laugh. Dan warmed up to the conversation and told several stories about working at the D.P.W. that kept the laughter going until we finally broke up around 8:30. For the first time, I had seen the humorous side of Dan. He loves to tell stories both on himself and his co-workers and laughed loud and affectionately.

Over the next few months I learned a lot more about Dan and Jen. He graduated with a degree in criminal justice and urban health from Georgia State University. Jen obtained her degrees from the University of South Carolina in Columbia. After living in Atlanta for several years, they sold their house and used the money to spend a year in Europe, primarily off the coast of Spain. They traveled extensively, visiting most of the countries in the world. India confirmed Dan's belief that humanity is one big pool of maggots.

Since Lisa was three years-old at the time, they decided to return to the States and moved in with Dan's parents in New Jersey. After reading an advertisement in the *New York Times,* Daniel began his career with mentally handicapped children in upstate New York. He is still in relationship with many of those kids. Cleo, the boy who learned to drive a tractor, calls often.

After the war, Dan grew obsessed with humanity's dark side and the capacity of one man to do damage to another. He read widely on the subject and found satisfaction in working with retarded children. When the AIDS epidemic unfolded in the mid-eighties, he decided he didn't want to watch the children die. Homosexuality is often rampant in segregated group homes, and he knew the possibilities of the disease taking the kids he cared for. He simply did not want to watch people he loved die, nor did he care for the silly isolationist rules government agencies often impose on loving children.

One May Sunday afternoon, he took Lisa to a boat show in New York. The short drive was made arduous because of the heavy snow still on the ground. After spending several hours admiring the boats, he resolved to move south "where you can put a boat in the water anytime you want to." The desire for a warmer climate, coupled with the concern of his kids being infected with AIDS, led him to conclude there is no problem too big to run from. It was time to "chuck it" all and move.

Dan and Jen had visited Tybee while they were dating, remembered it fondly, and decided to move to Georgia shortly after the boat show. Dan took employment with the D.P.W. at Tybee because he didn't want to take a job he couldn't walk home from. The friendship with Barry blossomed, and Dan discovered his love for the water.

"Most people don't like the water off Tybee because they don't understand it," he explained once. "They think because it's muddy there's nothing underneath. Once I was out, for some reason the water cleared. It was as transparent as the Gulf Stream. Looking down, I could see layers and layers of fish under the boat. This is the best water for fishing there is."

One morning Daniel walked into The Breakfast Club earlier than usual, grunted greetings, and took a seat at the counter. Opening his newspaper and sipping his coffee, he ordered his breakfast and consumed it before speaking. He cleared his throat and announced he would be going shark fishing over the next few days.

"Anyone want to go?" he asked.

Bill immediately volunteered to go as soon as possible. Daniel nodded his head and asked if anyone else wished to join them.

"I'll go," I said.

"Okay," he answered without glancing at me.

"Do you mind if my daughter Kristen comes along?" I asked. Kristen is fourteen years-old and the adventurer in the family. Extremely athletic and always willing to try something new, I knew she would love to tell her friends she was experienced at fishing for sharks.

We quickly scheduled the trip, and, several days later, Daniel took us out with him. His homemade boat looks like a big bathtub that floats. We left Criminal Creek around four o'clock and traveled to the third sea buoy, marking the entrance into the river channel. He explained that sharks feed during the cool of dusk on hot days, and high tide is the best time to fish. A brisk wind was blowing in from the ocean. The waves were high, causing the fourteen-foot tub to bounce up and down like a cork bobbing in the middle of a massive lake. It took an hour to travel the distance to Daniel's favorite fishing hole. By the time we arrived, Kristen and I had ricocheted from one side of the vessel to the other. Sitting in a boat rolling over large waves was preferable to crashing into them at high speed, however.

As the sun set, Daniel stood in the bow of the boat, throwing his anchor into the open sea. Kristen and I remained seated in the stern, looking at the larger-than-life D.P.W. sailor tug on the rope. The anchor would dig into the bottom so the boat would not drift. With the darkening sky over his shoulders, he appeared as a lonely soldier fighting the wind and sea, in command of what he could control and respectful of that which he could not.

"Being out here almost makes me believe in God," he said. "Once, I was fishing for shark when I hooked a tarpon. It was close to a hundred pounds, and there was a moment when it jumped out of the water trying to throw the hook from its mouth. His eye caught mine and, just for a moment, I knew there was a God."

When he had set the anchor, he opened the bucket of live mullet. He grabbed one, cut it so it would bleed, and skillfully ran the hook through its midsection. He repeated the procedure four times, dropping four lines. As the last one submerged into the dark brown water, he explained what would happen.

"First, you'll hear the clacking sound of the reel as the shark takes the hook. After he has it in his mouth, he'll start swimming with it, and you'll see he's taking line. At that point pick up the rod, push the lever that reverses the line, and jerk upwards so the hook sets in the shark's mouth. Second, reel him in fast. When you get him to the side of the boat, let me take over."

Kristen and I said we understood, and we waited. Daniel busied himself with the bait, other hooks, and making certain we were comfortable. Though the water was rough, we were so excited we did not notice. To my surprise, he was a graceful and attentive host. Every so often, a wave would pick the boat up only to drop it again. Whenever this happened, Daniel would calmly say, "That was a good roller."

After a few short minutes, Daniel said we should have had a bite. No sooner had the words come out of his mouth than one of the lines was struck. We heard a high pitch *ZIP* sound as the clacker signified that a shark had the bait in its mouth. Jumping to action I picked up the rod, turned the lever, waited a moment, and snapped it upwards. I turned the clacker off, worked the line, and reeled it in as quickly as I could. The heavy line pulled straight down, and I knew the shark was under the boat. I continued to reel it in until I saw a three-foot sand shark just below the water.

Moving swiftly, Daniel grabbed the rod from me and leaned over the side of the boat. Grabbing a stick with a large metal hook, he gaffed the shark, placing the crook through the gills until it came out of the mouth. Pulling it up so it rested on the side of the boat, he placed one hand behind the head, took out his knife, and prepared to win the battle he could control. The shark twisted and shook its body with frightening strength until Daniel subdued it. He asked if we wanted to keep it.

Kristen said yes, but I replied that I wouldn't know what to do with it. Daniel asked if we minded if he butchered one or two. We said we did not mind.

"They're for Robert Rowland," he explained as he cut off the shark's head. "He feeds them to his eighty-year-old mother who thinks they're sword fish. She'll ask if he's serving her shark, but he'll always say it's not. She has no idea what she's been eating all these years."

Robert Rowland was a worn-out city employee who also worked at the D.P.W. and lived alone with his mother. Daniel was forever telling stories at The Breakfast Club of working with Robert Rowland. I had never met Robert, but I deduced from the stories that he often placed himself in dubious situations with comical consequences.

After cutting off the shark's head, Daniel cut the stomach so he could gut the fish. The head dropped into the water, its jaws filled with rows of razor-sharp teeth, still biting at its conqueror. He also cut off the tail, leaving the torso flapping in the bottom of the boat. Blood covered the side and splattered on Daniel's bare legs.

"How long before it knows that it's dead?" Kristen asked.

"Oh, they can go on for an hour or so. A lot of people have been bitten by severed shark heads, and the body can go on for about as long. He rinsed the torso off in the ocean before tossing it in a cooler full of ice and soft drinks."

While we were waiting, a blue and white boat appeared excited. Daniel called our attention to it and said the people in it had also caught a shark. In the distance we observed one of the crew members pick up the animal, lifting it over his head and slamming it into the bottom of the boat. Again and again we saw the silver raised above the head and slammed onto the bottom of the boat.

"Another Tybee tradition," Daniel sighed.

"What's that?" Kristen and I asked.

"Oh, they believe you can kill a shark by hitting it like that, but it doesn't do any good. You've already seen they can live without their heads."

We nodded and turned our attention back to the lines. We fished for another hour or so but only caught one more shark. The sharks had eaten all of the bait from the three hooks. Frustrated, Daniel cut several mullet into bloody pieces and dropped them overboard in hopes of exciting the sharks. With only one baited hook left, Kristen reeled one in. Daniel cleaned it just as he had the first, throwing more blood into the boat.

"We're out of bait," he said as he started the motor, "and therefore we're out of time."

The return to the back river was easier because we were going in the same direction the wind was blowing. Inside the protective marshes, the water was smooth, and the boat swiftly glided us toward Daniel's house. Suddenly, he slowed and pointed to a pod of mating dolphins. Two dolphins circled each other, splashing as their bodies came together for a few brief seconds then separated to resume the splashing. The male would jump completely out of the water or stand on its tail, a "trick" I had assumed Sea World trainers had taught the creatures. Obviously, in the open sea no one taught dolphins much of anything. The boat stopped moving, and the dolphins plunged below the water. We waited and, surprisingly, their heads came out of the water and leaned over into the boat.

"I've seen dolphins do that at Sea World," Kristen said.

"Somebody's been feeding these dolphins," Daniel noted.

Across the Savannah River, Hilton Head Island sits on Calibogue Sound. The State of South Carolina does not prohibit humans from feeding dolphins, but the State of Georgia does. While we knew the difference between Georgia and South Carolina, the dolphins evidently did not.

"Let's see if they'll eat shark," Daniel offered, grabbing a torso from the cooler and handing it to Kristen.

She leaned over the water and offered several pounds of shark meat to the first dolphin that wanted to try it. Most people believe that if dolphins are present, sharks are somewhere else. The two species have little to do with each other. Sharks attack sick or dying fish only. A nine-foot dolphin that once washed ashore had several large gaping punctures from shark bites. It must have been sick for the sharks to attack it, as the friendly and ferocious animals maintain a respectful underwater relationship.

One of the dolphins seemed to leap from the water toward a startled Kristen, who dropped the shark into the water. The dolphins submerged for a few moments. We wondered if they were eating the meat. Daniel opened the cooler again and began fileting the meat.

"Let's try this," he said, offering us steaks for dolphin food.

We all held filets out for the dolphins, but they seemed to have lost interest and resumed their mating dance, splashing on the water's surface and doing Sea World tricks to impress each other.

"I guess this isn't a dinner date," Daniel mused as he again started the engine.

Making our way through the suddenly-calm marsh river, each person seemed to be lost in his or her own thoughts of the dolphins. Seeing the charm of the mating animals provoked an appreciation for the beauty of our surroundings. Nature seemed to be exploding around us. The brown-green marsh grass was brilliant as we sailed past. The black mud on the banks seemed illuminated, catching the sun's light and reflecting it toward the heavens. A flock of small tree swallows, steely blue-green wings spread over snowy white bodies, raced through the river with us, keeping pace with the boat. Everything was alive, and we were part of it.

When the boat docked, we unloaded the coolers, rods, and reels and proceeded to wash them. As we thanked Daniel for the experience, he said he would take us out anytime we wished. Driving home, I could not help but reflect on how perfect he is for Tybee. He typifies a lifestyle most people only wish they had the courage to live. Tybee is also the perfect place for Daniel. While many people dream of giving up the rat-race lifestyle, embracing a simpler pace, living on less, and moving to an island, Daniel and Jenny actually have done it. They chucked the world's values and forged their own.

Daniel is blessed with good education and job experiences and has a unique gift for working with special children. Jenny is also highly educated. Her occupational experiences attract others to her, and she has crossed the borders of the world. They could have had a very different life if they had chosen careers and a more conventional approach to life. Instead, they have purposely gravitated down the social spiral and landed on Tybee, living on the meager salary of a D.P.W. employee. Yet, they are far from poor. The ocean is their playground, their circle of friends is small but strong, and the nuisance of society's expectations are of no concern to them. They have a closeness with the island, not Tybee but the island itself. Others worry about the growth, politics, or beach erosion, but not Daniel. He simply enjoys the island. He has chucked everything else.

"Tis a gift to be simple, 'tis a gift to be free." Daniel and Jenny portray the words of this old Quaker hymn. They are the freest people I have ever met—and the richest.

Bicycle Joe

Most mornings the atmosphere is relaxed and playful at The Breakfast Club. The first shift solves most of the world's problems by 7:00 A.M. The second shift settles all of Tybee's difficulties. The third shift members try to solve their own problems. Occasionally, new members will show up, and eventually they are adopted into the family.

I'm a member of the first shift. Each morning, I meet two nurses, Frankie and Nancy; Daniel; James, a businessman; Johnny, who works for the City of Savannah; William; and Adam. For several years, we have collected around the coffee counter and jump-started each other's morning.

"Bicycle Joe" is the nickname he earned, as his only mode of transportation was the old rusty bike he found, somehow obtained parts for, and fixed up. Most of his worldly possessions were in the basket affixed to the handlebars; the rest were hidden in his "hootch" located somewhere near the old tower at the south end of Tybee. He showed up one morning, drinking coffee and saying he liked the island so much he was going to stay.

Joe rarely wore a shirt, and even when he did it was never buttoned. Several weeks prior the mayor and several council members accompanied the Tybee police to the Kitten's Corner, a striptease bar, to verify that dancers were indeed exposing their breasts. Each delegate reported this was indeed the case, and, of course, the following morning at The Breakfast Club we wanted to know when Joe was hired as a dancer at the Kitten's Corner. This typifies the collective humor of the first shift.

Joe was not employed. While he would never admit it, he was waiting on his appeal for assistance from the veteran's administration. Everyone knew he slept on the beach. He worked every day, helping Georgeanna deliver the papers, mowing someone's grass, or polishing brass and silverwear for people who had it and were willing to pay.

When he had enough money, he rented a room at the Seagull, Tybee's cheapest hotel. We could always tell when he slept outside because he was dirty, smelled a bit, and sand fell out of his hair all over the counter. Some mornings he asked if we could buy the coffee and he would pay for it next time. We're still waiting on the next time to arrive.

Joe was more than six-feet-tall, deeply tanned, and had a deformed right arm and his own sick sense of humor. One morning he was telling us that he had spent the previous night praying to God to make his arm like the other one. "Of course, you know what happened," he coaxed. "Now I have two deformed arms," and he curled his left arm so that it looked like the right one.

One afternoon I was jogging on the beach and heard someone call my name. It was Joe, motioning something with his deformed arm and looking serious. I was concentrating on other things as I ran and did not get the message to stop. I waived and picked up my pace. Like many people who run, I detest breaking my rhythm—in spite of the merits of stopping once in a while. When I arrived home, the phone was ringing. It was Joe. "I meant for you to stop. Can you spare a few moments? I need to talk to you."

Having just thrown Chelsea—my four-year-old—into the bathtub, and because no one else was home, I said that I could not meet him but could talk on the phone. Joe's response was a sigh.

"What's wrong?" I asked.

"You know I'm a veteran, right?"

I told him that I knew he was. I remembered picking him up next to William's Seafood one night as he thumbed his way to Tybee. He had said he was a medical discharge from the Marines and had served in Vietnam. I assumed that was the reason for the deformity of his right arm.

"Well, I was there when they were dumping Agent Orange, and I guess I got my fair share. Anyway, that's why my body is kind of bloated. It's hard finding shirts that fit."

Immediately I felt bad about all of those morning jokes. Joe had always laughed along with us.

"Anyway," he continued, "the doctors are telling me that I don't have much longer. I thought it was years, and they're talking like it's months. You're the only person I could think of to call." His voice cracked, and I heard him crying through the phone line.

"What do you need me to do?" I asked.

"I need a rabbi."

Bicycle Joe

"You're Jewish?"

"Do you know one?"

I told him to give me the phone number of where he was and I would see what I could do. I hung up the phone and called a rabbi friend who immediately called Joe. They talked for almost an hour. Later, I called the rabbi to find out if I needed to do anything. Before responding to my question, he wanted to know some things about Joe.

"He's homeless. He evidently was exposed to Agent Orange. I see him most mornings at The Breakfast Club. He works as much as he can. He's a likable fellow, and he wanted a rabbi."

The rabbi recounted their conversation. "Joe's afraid to meet his maker. He killed a great many people in Vietnam. He told me some of the stories. They're horrible. There was one little girl . . ." He paused, unable to convey the terror of the images.

"What do you think?" I asked.

"His name is Joseph Leftov. It is an interesting name. Leftov means 'good heart' in Hebrew. I think that's the root of his struggle. His good heart can't get over the killing."

When the regulars at The Breakfast Club learned this information about Joe, the teasing ceased instantly, and folks began helping Joe. Georgeanna was the first, of course, having already hired him to help deliver the newspapers. They were often seen together, riding in her truck or pulled off the side of the road rolling the papers and placing a rubber band around them. After a while the teasing began again, but this time it centered around the suspicion that the two were developing a romantic relationship. Georgeanna threatened to kill us, and Joe decided he would rather quit than be too closely associated with her.

James hired Joe to help out around his job, but Joe kept messing things up. Most everyone hired Joe to polish whatever silver or brass they had, but eventually everything had been polished. Jordy even hired him as the dishwasher, but Joe could not keep up with the demand. He quit that job, too.

One morning Joe did not show. Several people asked where he was, but no one was particularly concerned that he wasn't there that morning. He was not there the next day either, and we all asked one another where he might be. When Georgeanna arrived, we learned that he had gone.

"What do you mean, he's gone?" we asked.

"Yeah, there were some tourists here from Pittsburgh—that's where he's from—and he caught a ride with them."

"He caught a ride with some strangers to Pittsburgh? That's not like catching a ride to town."

"He came by to see me before he left. That was his story."

"Why did he leave?"

She shrugged her shoulders but didn't say anything.

Rarely does someone choose to leave Tybee if they don't have to. People will complain for days if their company transfers them to another city or family concerns cause them to return to another place. The Breakfast Club easily embraces those who come and stay; and it doesn't take long for the circle to close again, and new faces begin to replace those who have left.

The daily rituals continue, of course. Life goes on. At The Breakfast Club, each new day is celebrated with good friends and coffee. Like many families, history is passed on through storytelling. Joe is still remembered around the counter, and his name is brought up every once in a while. Several months after he had gone, Johnny told me he had received a phone call from someone pretending to be Joe's lawyer.

Sunset and Sea Oats

Bicycle Joe

"Joe's lawyer?" I asked. "What was that about?"

"Oh, it was Joe, pretending to be Joe's lawyer. I know that voice, and it was Joe. I asked him what in the world he was doing trying to fool me like that."

"What did he say?"

"Oh, something about Joe being dead and how nice we had been to him down here, and he wanted to let us know about him being dead and all."

"But you didn't believe him?" I asked, remembering what the rabbi had told me.

"Hell, no," Johnny quickly said, "it was Joe. I just don't know why he would want to pull a stupid stunt like that. He may have been a pain in the ass, but we liked him."

After a few moments of silence, I commented that it may have been a lawyer who called. "Sometimes we forget what people sound like."

"No," he cut me off, "Joe had a peculiar voice. I recognized him."

We sat in silence, sipping our coffee and trying to catch up on the conversation that had transpired around us. Daniel had taken Bill shark fishing, and we were hearing a colorful description of how crazy a hooked shark acts when pulled beside a boat. Johnny interrupted me again.

"You know, a lot of people in Pittsburgh have peculiar voices. I still think it was Joe, but I suppose it could have been a lawyer."

The Church of the Breakfast Club

Most small towns have at least one place where locals show up for early morning coffee and breakfast. Everyone seems to know each other, and the meal is an excuse to slide into another day amidst friends. The waitress knows what the regulars want without asking, and meals are specially prepared to the customer's specific taste.

Typically these places are small and intimate, creating a friendly environment for friends to engage in conversation with one another. Morning conversations are normally quiet until several gallons of coffee have been consumed. Then, as the caffeine starts to kick in, discussions become lively. Topics range from politics to whatever was on television the night before to sports to local gossip. Should a stranger enter, an immediate silence envelopes the place so that the regulars can look the newcomer over. When the stranger is seated, the conversation will resume in quiet tones and then build back to the level prior to the intrusion.

These institutions have names like the "Chew and Chat," "Squat and Gobble," "The Eating Place," or "Hank's Double Loop." In Savannah, "Clary's Cafe" is an upscale version of the small town establishments, and "Larry's Restaurant" comes closest to what we have on Tybee. None are connected with the national chain franchises that command the most attention with their "feed as many as you can in the shortest possible time" philosophy. Like the towns where they are found, these special establishments are low-key and warm. While all of them are good, The World Famous Breakfast Club on Tybee Island is the best.

I'm not certain how The Breakfast Club got to be world famous. I've never spotted any world dignitaries eating a waffle beside me or seen a full page review in the *New York Times*, although The Breakfast Club has been written up on numerous occasions in restaurant trade publications such as the *Athens (Georgia) Daily Banner* and the *Atlanta Constitution*. People will drive the seventeen miles from Savannah to Tybee just to eat breakfast and, if the weather is nice, take a morning stroll on the beach. While this devoted following is evident now, the genesis of The Breakfast Club would never have indicated such a fondness.

Situated on the corner of Fifteenth Street and Butler Avenue, the building was originally constructed as a storage area for the old Tybee railroad. In the early 1970s, it was converted to a beachside hamburger stand, quite small with seven booths and a counter with stools for fourteen other customers. A huge sign proclaimed "MONSTER BURGERS," with a blue and white drawing of a monster holding a hamburger. These were really good burgers, but the seasonal flow of tourists did not sustain the effort.

In 1976 Agnes Prochowski purchased the restaurant and named it The Breakfast Club. Still focusing on hamburgers for the early morning hangover and lunch crowds, she displayed a sign in the windows with a picture of a hamburger and the words "We Roll Our Own!"

Agnes was not a typical restaurant owner, nor was she especially prepared for the headaches that go along with operating a business in food services. The biggest problem was her mouth. Whenever things went wrong, as they often do in a restaurant, she would cuss like a sailor— which, of course, endeared her to the salty saints of Tybee Island. Whenever she dropped an egg, the air conditioner broke, or the dishwasher did not show up, Agnes would use profanity that would embarrass Eddie Murphy. No matter what happened, she would begin to cuss and cuss and cuss. Regulars were used to it, but tourists would cover their children's ears, quickly pay the bill, and leave. The regulars would roar with laughter.

Of course, this alone was not enough to attract a following, but Agnes had her husband Roy. A tall, thin man who drank too much for his own good, Roy had physical problems that left him pretty lethargic, sitting silent and alone on the last counter stool. People began to refer to him as Lurch, the butler in the television series "The Addams Family."

To complete the package, Agnes's daughter cooked at The Breakfast Club in the early days. Prior to helping her mother, she had fled Chicago and then joined a "moonie"-type cult farther west. The cult demanded that followers shave their heads and vow to never leave their new-found religion. After several months, however, she came to Tybee where she helped her mother in the restaurant. In 1976 few women shaved their heads, and Tybee had certainly never seen such a sight.

The Church of the Breakfast Club

Taken together, the owner who cussed like a sailor, her listless Frankenstein husband who rarely moved in his seat, and the bald lady were enough to charm many of the eccentrics on Tybee. This was not enough, however, to make the restaurant particularly profitable, and the Prochowskis knew they would not make it without help.

Agnes Prochowski knew where to turn to help the business. She made an offer to her son in Phoenix that he could not refuse. In return for leaving Phoenix and living on a coastal island where winter lasts about three months, he would be the principal "partner" in charge of all operations of the restaurant. The deal was struck, and Jordan Prochowski left Phoenix, Arizona, and moved to the warm breezes of Tybee Island. He had just enough money to get to the island and ran out of gas as soon as he crossed the city limits.

The tall, thin, muscular, sandy-haired chef is the principal difference between The Breakfast Club and other small town establishments. Most have cooks; The Breakfast Club has a chef. A graduate of Chicago's Culinary Institute of America, he has received numerous awards and honors for his tasty creations. Upon moving to Tybee in 1982, he immediately took charge. Recognizing that there were few breakfast options on the island, Jordy resolved this would be the primary meal served. Recalling his mother's meal for the help who had worked as dishwashers, bus boys, and clean up, he named the first special "Agnes's Solidarity"—which was the old grill cleaner's special—a concoction of eggs and whatever was left over that day.

Jordy is one of the few people who have mastered the art of preparing grits, no small feat for a northerner. Most people who prepare grits, including many southerners, do not salt them properly and leave it to the customer to determine if butter is needed. Jordy knows better. He can prepare perfectly salted grits and serves a mountain of the corn pone on the plate, swimming in a sea of butter. For survival in the South, this importance of grits at breakfast cannot be overly estimated. The late columnist Lewis Grizzard once wrote:

> The reason Yankees don't like grits is nobody ever told 'em how to eat 'em. If you don't doctor up grits a little, I'll be the first to admit they taste like something I wouldn't even say.[1]

Being the great chef he is, Jordy knows such things; and the grits are always perfect.

133

The other major difference between The Breakfast Club and other small town restaurants is that it has a theme. Entering The Breakfast Club is much like walking into a Wrigley Field souvenir shop. To claim Jordy is a Cubs fan is a serious understatement. Like most Cubs fans, he worships the team.

A life-size poster of first baseman Mark Grace holding a carton of milk graces the walls. A framed photograph of Wrigley Field is displayed prominently. Framed baseball cards, including one of Jordy in a Cubs uniform, adorn another wall. Whenever a customer happens to be wearing a Cubs hat or jersey, he or she gets breakfast on the house! To be a Cubs fan at The Breakfast Club is to embody the words of famed Cub broadcaster Harry Carey when describing Wrigley Field: "Every day is Mardi Gras, and every fan is a king."[2]

This brings up another difference between The Breakfast Club and other establishments. Because the grill is in plain view of most customers, Jordy recognizes the need for showmanship in preparing one's breakfast. On weekdays two chefs prepare meals, and on weekends three. Watching them prepare ten or fifteen meals at the same time is to appreciate the finesse of the choreographed effort of a ballet production or a basketball team.

First-time customers are mesmerized as Jordy works the center of the grill, cracking eggs with one hand, flipping omelets with the other, and appearing to do a thousand different things at one time. Bill—Jordy's number-two chef—runs the waffle irons to the right, prepares all of the ingredients for the specials, and throws hamburgers on the grill. Brian—who will attend Notre Dame University—prepares the toast and dispenses the plates to the waitresses, yelling out the numbers of the order.

Collectively, they are seen as a blur of flying arms, discarded egg shells, and hands placing things on the grill and seemingly picking them up at the same time. They laugh, sing, and joke as they work their masterpieces. From time to time, Jordy will reach for an egg and suddenly throw it at an unsuspecting customer. The startled man or woman will jump out of the way only to watch the rubber egg bounce safely to the floor. One of the regulars retrieves the rubber orb, and again it is placed among the real eggs for the next unsuspecting customer.

While most breakfast restaurants have only one or two outrageous personalities on staff, everyone at The Breakfast Club could work as a professional entertainer. Bill, for example, would be a radio sports show host. A sports enthusiast who will engage in endless conversations about whatever sport happens to be in season, he does prep work by subscribing to several hundred sports magazines that he studies nightly. Early each morning, before the rush begins around eight o'clock, he will hold forth with the audience of regulars and lecture on basketball's Final Four, the best hitter in baseball, and which horse he likes in the Kentucky Derby.

No one takes it as serious as Bill does, and he is rarely challenged. Unlike most radio sports commentators, however, he loses all objectivity during football season. He is from Texas and worships the Dallas Cowboys. Mention the Cowboys and Bill will immediately launch into a discourse on every fact, scenario, or wish open to the team at the time. Unlike many fans, he is not a sore loser; and when the Cowboys are defeated, he is as good-natured as anyone about it. When asked about his reactions to such a loss, he mildly states that he got it out of his system after the game by trashing his trailer.

Barry, the head waiter and brother of Jordy's wife, could host his own television fishing program on Sunday afternoons. The driver of an eighteen-wheeler truck for many years, the toil of too many years on the road had cost Barry his family, and Chicago just didn't mean as much alone.

When Jordy called asking for help with The Breakfast Club, Barry jumped at the chance and moved to the island. In those days there was no longer the draw of the lady who cussed, Frankenstein, and the bald cook; so Barry and Jordy spent many days alone in their restaurant. Often it was so bad that the two of them would throw a frisbee in the street because no one was in the restaurant. If a lone customer did arrive, they would merely tell him to help himself until they were finished.

When he was inside, Barry's hands and life were often in danger. As an experienced trucker, he knew nothing about cooking in a restaurant so, as he chopped onions, he often took pieces of his fingers off as well. People began showing up simply to see if they would get a meal or observe a self-sacrifice behind the counter. He had the personality Jordy needed, however, to engage customers and make them feel they made the best decision of their lives when they entered The Breakfast Club.

Because the restaurant opened early and closed after lunch, Barry found he was free in the afternoons. He took up fishing and discovered what he had missed in Chicago all those years. The Breakfast Club allowed Barry to fully explore his love for salt water fishing. He went deep sea fishing as often as possible, making the ninety-mile trip to the Gulf Stream, but fell in love with the marshes. Increasingly, the topic of conversation at The Breakfast Club centered around where the fish were biting and how Barry was doing dropping the line. Tybee had a large population of fishermen who began making The Breakfast Club their second home, because when they were not on the water, they could at least talk about it.

In recent years Barry has decided he wants to keep his fingers, so he no longer cooks but is the chief waiter and staff supervisor. He became a good cook, but is a better waiter. He is now able to spend more time talking about fishing without having to concentrate on whether or not he's burning the food.

Jean has a master's degree in art, and when she is not painting or traveling around the world, she is a waitress. When Amy was visiting Tybee for a weekend, she left a note on Barry's truck asking him out. They had the date, married, and now she is a waitress at The Breakfast Club. Jeannine is Bill's sister and, after coming to visit him for a few days, saw that Bill needed help putting the trailer pack together after the Cowboys lost, so she decided to stay. She tried working a real job and decided it would be more fun to be a waitress. Besides, it sometimes takes quite some time to put the trailer back in order.

During the summer my wife Janice, a schoolteacher most of the time, is a waitress. She was "invited" to work at The Breakfast Club because Barry and Bill like her a great deal and have asked her to move out of our house so she can fish or pull for the Cowboys with them.

Tourist season also separates The Breakfast Club from other places. Normally, regulars begin to arrive at six every morning. A sprinkling of tourists may or may not be present at this time of the day. By eight o'clock, however, tourists descend in droves. Oftentimes, families quietly take a booth and enjoy the great meals served.

With regularity during the spring and summer, some wayfarer who has spent too much time in Tybee's bars ends his or her night by having breakfast. Taking a seat at the counter, this person is loud and obnoxious and may attempt to sweet-talk one of the waitresses or simply dominate the morning conversation: "Say, how many of you sandy butts ever milk a cow?"

"Why would anyone want to milk a cow when they can simply walk to the store and buy a gallon?" Johnny replies.

The visitor will normally retreat into silence for a few minutes before asking other such penetrating questions. For example, Jordy has been asked if he knows how to prepare omelets like that little place—he can't remember the name right now—outside of Akron, Ohio. Other illustrations of these astute queries actually heard while sitting around the counter are:

The Church of the Breakfast Club

—What is the difference between the Georgia lottery and the Florida lottery?
—Can I get breakfast here?
—How do I get to the ocean from here?
—What is a grit?

Such questions are normally taken in stride. From mid-April until early September, however, the number of tourists and, therefore, the number of such interrogations increase.

These episodes would be manageable were it not for the fact that most residents of Savannah are fascinated with The Breakfast Club and on weekends will drive seventeen miles just to eat breakfast. Literally hundreds of folks make this drive and are considered to be bootleg regulars. If Savannah has a unique love affair with Tybee, it has fallen into absolute lust with The Breakfast Club. Folks come for the food and a walk on the beach afterwards. For many of them, a trip to Tybee is not complete without stopping at The Breakfast Club.

Taken all together, the regulars, the tourists and the bootleggers from Savannah create a mad house where lines form on the sidewalk as people wait to get inside. Anticipation builds to sometimes unrealistic levels, but Jordy never seems to fail to please.

Several groups of people are as devoted to The Breakfast Club as a fundamentalist Baptist deacon is faithful to his church or a wino is dedicated to his bottle, both of which are actually represented in the regulars. Most every day of their lives begins with the early morning advent at the restaurant.

Entering two or three at a time, they congregate around the beloved counter. No regular customer sits in a booth unless he or she absolutely must. Unfortunately, sometimes there are no vacant seats at the counter, and someone is confined to the wilderness of the booth, where the regulars feel the devil sends tourists for torment.

The sad expression on the face of a late-arriving regular on a crowded morning is enough to make grown men and women cry. It is not so for the chosen few who sit at the counter. The commitment of the regulars is such that they will wake up at ungodly hours of the morning to arrive early enough to obtain one of the chosen counter seats. These seats are close together, and one can sit with fifteen of his or her closest friends, communing and sharing coffee—the holy elixir of life.

Regulars will then share orders of the bread of life: rye toast or a grilled English muffin. Many mornings, while Barry or Bill are reading the morning paper, regulars enter the inner sanctum and share fresh coffee, pouring it freely for the other members of the fellowship. They begin to testify with stories from their lives that are usually affirmed with laughter and additional confirmations from others. Finally, as the time draws nigh, final words of encouragement are offered: "Have a nice day," "Drive carefully," or "Don't do what I wouldn't do."

If a member is absent, the other regulars fret, worry, and pray that everything is all right. Oftentimes, they even make home visits. For them, it is not merely a place to begin their day; it is the Church of The Breakfast Club.

Three shifts of customers show up, more or less, daily at The Breakfast Club. From 6:00 to 7:00 A.M., the first shift arrives. Georgeanna has finished delivering newspapers and sits at the corner of the counter. Beside her is Frankie, a nurse who is preparing to make the drive into town and quietly reads the paper and eats her breakfast. James operates his own business on the island and is always prepared to make a sale, even before his first cup of coffee. Johnny rambles on about whatever Rush Limbaugh said the day before. Wilson drives in from Wilmington Island every morning so he can tell everyone how they used to do things in Cleveland.

Daniel, the shark fisherman, and his wife, Jenny, arrive at seven. Daniel works as a general employee for the City of Tybee and hopes it will resume garbage pickup and cease contracting that service. He wants to finish his psychological analysis of people and their garbage.

The primary mainstay and master of ceremonies of the morning shift is William, a retired Navy man who lost most of his hearing in the early testing of nuclear bombs. William is a seventy-year-old man who laughs, jokes, provokes, and plays with everyone. If Jordy is the high priest of The Breakfast Club, William is the prophet—or at least the mouthpiece.

Originally from Buffalo, William's family moved to Tybee when he was quite small. He was raised on the island and is, therefore, the counter historian. He has also been a member of The Breakfast Club congregation since the day Agnes opened the place. "When did you start coming here?" someone will ask.

"Well, I drove by this place for years," he explains, "but never bothered to stop in. One morning my brother asked me to help him do something, and, once we finished, he suggested we get some breakfast. We came here, and I really hit it off with Agnes, Jordy's mom. I've been coming ever since."

The Church of the Breakfast Club

A Washington Redskins football fan, William and Bill have a friendly rivalry each fall. They place five-dollar bets on the outcome of the Cowboys-Redskins games. Should the Redskins happen to win, Bill will ignore William until the old man can no longer stand it and walk up to the chef who is chopping onions or peeling potatoes and say, "Excuse me sir, but I believe you have something that belongs to me."

Bill will smile, shake William's hand, dig the wallet from his white uniform, and hand William the five-dollar bill. Smiling and shaking hands, it is easy to see the two are genuine friends. They proceed to discuss the game for several minutes until William returns to his seat, slaps the money on the counter, and proclaims loudly, "The coffee's on Bill!"

Should the Cowboys win the game, however, William will go to make-believe extremes to not pay Bill the bet. He has been known to dress as a tourist with oversize sun glasses, a Cowboys fan complete with hats and shirts, a woman with long hair in a dress, and a number of other poor disguises. Quietly taking his seat, Bill will lay his prep knife aside and walk up to the stranger. A few moments of delightful silence follow, until William pulls out the five dollar bill, smiles, cusses, and hands over the money. Bill normally puts it in his pocket and proclaims, "The coffee's on William!"

William is impossible to describe. If anyone has had a birthday, anniversary, or night of special significance, he and his wife Frances remember the occasion by giving gifts and focusing everyone's attention on the distinctive event. He loves children, calling them "the little guys," and magically pulls half dollars from their ears. He is the principal prankster of the morning shift, cutting out amusing cartoons from the newspaper and writing in the names of regulars. He kisses on Georgeanna and just about anyone else who will let him each morning. Once when Georgeanna announced she could not wait to get home, take off her bra, and go to bed, he looked at her and said, "That explains it."

"Explains what?" she asked.

"Those two thuds I hear every morning about nine o'clock."

Everyone laughed as she hit him, although Georgeanna was smiling too.

Being a regular patron of The Breakfast Club is more like an extended family than merely a customer of a restaurant. Because there are several shifts of regulars, of course, the family is a lot larger from Jordy's perspective than from those seated at the counter. While it is work for the employees, they also display a great deal of affection, along with other characteristics of a family. Support, chastisement, jokes, sympathy, and genuine love are expressed on a daily basis. When one of the regulars experiences a tragedy in his or her life, the others respond like a family would.

Lisa, the daughter of Daniel and Jenny, was recently in a serious automobile accident. On the very day the collision occurred, regulars began notifying one another, visiting the hospital waiting room, and offering to do whatever they could to help. Because Daniel and Jenny had gone to the hospital as soon as they heard the news, Barry broke into their home to pack their bags, grab eyeglasses, books, and medicine they would need over the next several days. The phantom, that unknown figure who delivers gifts to islanders in times of distress, had a small present delivered.

Whenever Daniel and Jenny came into The Breakfast Club, normally before they went to the hospital, their meals were on the house. At once, they were declared winners of the betting pool, consisting of some seventy dollars to help them pay for gasoline for the daily travels into town. (The regulars will start a pool whenever Wilson gets a job. The bet is how long he will keep it. Of course, Wilson doesn't know the pool exists.)

Tybee Lighthouse

The Church of the Breakfast Club

The Breakfast Club became "information central" on Lisa's status during the next several weeks. When Lisa was finally released from the medical center, her first visit was to The Breakfast Club. Even the most dysfunctional families often pull together in times of crisis, and it was no different for this one.

Because The Breakfast Club is the place for dispensing of news, William's announcement one morning caught me off guard. In utter seriousness, he asked if I could drop by his house that evening around seven. Because the Beach Bum Parade was only a few weeks away, I was certain he and Frances had been chosen to be king and queen, a dubious honor as these were the first to be bombarded with water balloons. I could think of no one else, however, who deserved recognition and happily told him I would stop by after work.

William and Frances live in a quiet house on Ninth Street. Each holiday brings out the special decorations of the season. During Easter, the yard is filled with eggs and bunnies. At Christmas, candy canes, elves, and Santas contend for attention. On Valentine's Day, hearts hang on the door. During Halloween, ghosts and goblins of every form and shape dare trick-or-treaters to call. Even if there is no special occasion, the yard is filled with ceramic deer, gnomes, and fresh flowers.

Automobile tags from each of their years together hang over the door of William's shop, a tool shed where he fixes whatever neighbors have that need fixing. An old bathtub painted with flowers sits beside the driveway and is filled with fish or flowers, depending on whether or not the fish lived. Once I asked for directions to his house and was told to simply go to Ninth Street and stop at the house that looks like William and Frances's. There was no doubt about it when I drove by.

If the exterior of the house looks like a South Georgia town's version of the botanical gardens, the inside leaves one wondering if he or she has been mysteriously transported to a home in a small German hamlet. Clocks and antique furniture abound. Some eighty clocks of all shapes and sizes from every corner of the world possess each inch of wall space. Cuckoos and grandfathers, mantle pieces and railroad station wall compositions, silver, brass, wood, and glass are everywhere.

What space the clocks leave, Frances has filled with her own paintings, sewing, and artifacts collected from Africa—where she and William spent many years while he was in the Navy. They collect cans on Tybee and, when his truck is filled, trade them for cash to finance their trips across the country. Many islanders even recycle their beer cans by taking them to William and Frances. The house is small, intimate, and warm, and invites all who enter to be comfortable and feel at ease.

We sat around the large oak table, and Frances served a homemade pie and fresh coffee. If William is an exercise in childlike humor, Frances is the personification of southern gentility. She has a childlike quality, greeting everyone with a warm hug and a kiss and going out of her way to make everyone feel as though they are all part of the same big family. Her hobby is sewing, which is done in half of a workshop that is built onto the front of the house. The other half of the shop belongs to William's desk, littered with tools and parts of clocks.

Frankie and her husband Chuck arrived and, after everyone was settled, William grabbed Frances's hands and grew strangely silent. William's weather-worn face, filled with the lines and creases of being baked in the ocean sun, was full of pain. Frances had tears in her eyes. The silence was uncomfortable, and I found myself shifting in my seat.

"You all know," he began, carefully choosing his words, "that Frances and I have been very close to the Jones family for some time. We eat dinner with them every Friday night and often watch their little girl, Michelle. Well, several weeks ago I got a phone call around seven o'clock from Chief Polk at the police department. I've known him for years and thought my brother was in trouble or he needed my help on something. I went down there, and they sat me in a little room."

Pausing, he squeezed Frances's hands as tears flowed freely from her eyes into her lap. Frankie and Chuck sat stoically across from me. The silence was deafening.

"Well," he continued in a cracking voice, "the chief told me Michelle had told somebody at her school she had been molested. The school called some social workers who put it all on videotape. He said he had seen the tape, and Michelle told them I had touched her breasts and fondled them as I tucked her in bed one night."

He was quiet again, and his tears mixed with Frances's falling freely on their grasped hands. Frankie reached across the table and stroked Frances on the back. Chuck and I nodded our heads.

"Anyway, the chief said he was sorry but he had to charge me with one count of child molestation. It's going to be in tomorrow's paper, so I won't be at The Breakfast Club." Again the silent tears fell as William fought to compose himself.

The Church of the Breakfast Club

"You are our dear friends, and I don't want you to be surprised when you read tomorrow's paper. The other thing I wanted to tell you is I didn't do it." His voice grew firm but was still filled with sadness. "Michelle has spent a hundred nights with us, and I guess I've tucked her in a hundred times. I never did anything like that, and I don't know why she said it. We love them like our own family, and that's what hurts us so bad. Why would she say something like that? I want you to know I didn't do anything like that to the little guy."

Chuck spoke up before the silence could fill the room again. "I heard about it several days ago, and I want you to know I didn't believe it then, and I don't believe it now." Frankie immediately echoed her own affirmation of their friendship. Frances whispered, "Thank you, thank you" to either God or Chuck and Frankie.

I tried to visualize William doing such a thing and just couldn't imagine it. I thought of the many times my daughters, Chelsea and Kristen, had been alone with William and felt they would have told me if anything like this had ever happened. I looked at the pain and hope in the eyes of William and Frances. I did not notice the silence filling the room, but they did. Finally I broke the quiet.

"I believe you, William."

When I arrived at The Breakfast Club the next morning, the counter was empty. Two of the booths were jammed with regulars reading the newspaper. I knew what they were reading and walked past them directly to the coffee pot. Pouring myself a cup, I took a stool at the counter and wished everyone a good morning. Frankie soon followed suit.

"Have you seen the paper?" someone asked.

We told them that we had.

"Do you believe it?"

"No. Do you?"

Georgeanna was seated in one of the booths and shot a convincing glance at me. "Hell no, I don't believe it. I've known William a long time, and I know that crazy Jones clan. William ain't done it. The little brat is just wanting some attention from her old man."

Several conversations started at once. Some sided with Georgeanna, while others continued to express their disbelief. I noticed Jordy was not moving with his normal lightening speed, but pensively sipped a cup of coffee. The debate escalated around us, and Jordy disappeared into a back room. Seeing Barry at the far end of the room, I approached him and asked what he thought.

"What's going on?" I asked.

Blowing smoke from his cigarette, Barry appeared reflective as he answered. "We know everyone involved, and it's tough being a friend at times like this. Of course, we want what's best for Michelle. If she says she's been hurt, then we believe something happened and want her to be taken care of. We also know William and don't believe he did it. We're just not sure what to do. We believe Michelle, but we also believe William."

"Have you talked to William?"

"William came in late yesterday and told us," he explained. "Jordy told him that it didn't matter if it was true or not. We're friends. If William did do it, then we forgive him; and if he didn't, then it doesn't matter." The Church of The Breakfast Club had already dispensed forgiveness, and the sun hadn't even come up yet.

After work that day, I stopped at William and Frances's house for a visit. Frances was outside placing a cooler of soft drinks on top of her trash cans. She got in this habit as a way of thanking the garbage men for their efforts. I asked if we could talk for a few minutes. Inside the house was dark, and the phone was off the hook. William was taking a nap. We again sat at the heavy kitchen table. I wanted to know if they had a lawyer.

"Yes," Frances replied, "we found one the other day."

I wanted to know who it was, but she could not recall his name. "Isn't it someone you know?" I asked.

"No, we found him in the yellow pages."

"In the yellow pages!" I almost screamed.

"He had a real nice ad," she said, bewildered at my sudden loss of self-control. "Here, let me show you," and she opened the phone book to the advertisement.

"Frances, this is not the way you pick an attorney."

At first she seemed at a loss for words, then spoke very carefully. "We have lived either in Africa or on Tybee all of our lives. We don't know any attorneys. We studied all of the advertisements and thought this was the nicest."

I shook my head and scribbled down the counselor's name and phone number and asked Frances if she would care if I called. She thanked me for wanting to and confided that because William couldn't hear too well, she was worried he might not have understood everything they needed to know. The next morning, I called the lawyer's office and got an answering machine.

Later in the morning, Barry called from The Breakfast Club to ask if I wanted to go boating with him and Bill.

"Sure, when?" I asked.

"About an hour," he replied.

I am very conscientious about my work, leaving The Breakfast Club each morning around seven o'clock, stopping by the house for a few minutes to help Janice get the kids and herself off, and arriving at my post by 7:30. I had been after Barry and Bill to take me to the little lighthouse for sometime, and, being spontaneous sorts, they were calling. Both were off that day and planned to just take it easy in the boat.

"I'll bring the beer," I volunteered, as I hung up the receiver and quickly collected my things. By 10:15 I was at the Chimney Creek fish camp and parked beside the green trailer they called home. Looking at the twelve-pack I had brought, Barry said it wasn't enough—we would be out at least three hours. Stopping by the fish camp, they purchased another twelve-pack and loaded it into the cooler, and we were off.

Barry guided the small homemade boat through the rivers in the marshes to the open sea, hoping he would be able to navigate the vessel just off the beach, but the seas were too rough. Turning the dinghy around, we made our way through the marshes to the river channel where the little lighthouse sits.

Crossing the Lazaretto Creek bridge to Tybee, one is greeted with a panoramic view of the island and the ocean. To the right are the marshes, spread out like a flat plain of sea grass. Straight ahead is the island, with rooftops, evergreen trees, shrimp boats, and the big lighthouse. To the left is the ocean. Hilton Head Island can be seen in the distance. Nearby is the little lighthouse, an abandoned three-story structure without a light. At high tide the water covers the small patch of land on which the lighthouse rests, barring any who may wish to visit. At low tide, however, the ocean recedes and allows ample space for a small boat to beach so that visitors may enter the lighthouse. Taken altogether, the view from the top of the bridge is breathtaking.

After we landed the boat, we climbed to the small door on the west side of the lighthouse and entered. A crumbling and water-logged stone stairway circled its way almost to the top, where the bricks had fallen away and an old homemade wooden ladder led through a tiny trap door. After climbing up,

145

we stood on a new plywood floor. Another small opening led outside to the circular platform surrounding the top of the lighthouse. On the exterior, Barry opened three beers and invited me to enjoy the greatest view. We sat with our feet hanging off the side and toasted Tybee.

"Come on; there's one more thing I want to show you," Barry invited, offering a hand to pull me up. He proceeded to climb on top of the diminutive black iron ball that is the pinnacle of the structure.

"There's only a handful of people in the entire world who can claim to have done this!" he called.

He sat there for a full five minutes yelling at cars crossing the Lazaretto Creek bridge. "I can do this, and you can't!" he called and laughed.

Bill smiled and nursed his beer. "I don't care what those commercials say," he told me. "It just doesn't get any better than this!"

"Now it's your turn," Barry exclaimed as he jumped down.

He and Bill carefully stood watch as I climbed to the top of the structure. I concentrated on not falling on the millions of broken shells surrounding the base of the building. Once seated, however, the feeling was overwhelming. The ocean was to my back, the island spread out before me, and I literally felt I was on top of the world. Looking down into the water, a school of dolphins happily swam past.

"Dolphins!" Bill yelled. "Come on; let's go with them."

Barry and Bill all but pulled me off the lighthouse, and we quickly rushed down the stairs to the boat. As we pulled away, Barry said he wanted to bring all of his friends back and have a photographer take a picture of everyone on top of the little lighthouse and make the picture into Christmas cards and mail them to everyone who likes a white Christmas.

"That would be cruel," I said.

"Well, they need to know there's more than one way to have a white Christmas."

"How's that?"

"Snow is white, but sand is, too. It's all in how cold you want to be at Christmas."

I appreciated his judgment. We spent the next hour following the school of dolphins through the marsh rivers, often seeing them swim beside the boat and sometimes seeing them dive directly underneath and come up on the other side. Barry laid down in the back of the boat, steered with his feet, and claimed he was one with the universe.

The Church of the Breakfast Club

Around three o'clock, Bill noted we were down to the last couple of beers: "Just enough to make it back home." With this motivation, Barry skillfully directed the boat back to Chimney Creek. Once there, Bill and Barry proclaimed that it was time for a nap and entered the old green trailer. I thanked them for the trip and drove to William and Frances's house.

William and Frances were seated at the kitchen table and talking quietly. They asked if I wanted some coffee. I declined and asked what was the latest news.

"He has to be in court tomorrow," Frances told me. "We're pretty scared."

"Do you want me to go?" I offered.

"Would you?" they both asked at the same time.

So the next morning at nine in the morning, I met them at the Chatham County courthouse. Obviously nervous, Frances sat with William's sister, Rachel; and William paced the floor. Under his arms, he held the medals he had received in the Navy. Wilson, the know-it-all from Cleveland, was also present, dispelling several stereotypes I had of him. I asked William and Frances if they had talked to the attorney yet and was told he should be there any minute.

Twenty minutes after the designated time, a chubby, well-dressed man approached and introduced himself as their attorney. Frances asked Wilson to sit with her and Rachel while William and I discussed matters with his counselor.

"Look," he began, "I've viewed the tape several times, and the little girl simply states you touched her breasts and kissed her on the side of the mouth. The social workers did a lot of coaching, so I believe the judge will be very lenient with you."

"But I didn't do anything," William emphasized.

The attorney continued his explanation. "Unfortunately, in matters of child abuse, the laws are such that if a child makes this kind of claim, the courts are going to side with the child, even if there is no further evidence."

"What are you saying?" I asked.

"I'm saying he can plead not guilty if he wants to, but it will probably be a long, drawn-out court case. Even if the case does not go to trial, the charge will stand. In fact, even if she recants, it will still stand."

"So what should I do?" William asked.

"There is a plea where you tell the court that you are not guilty, but because of your age and the expense of a trial, you are not contesting the charge."

"But I'm not guilty," William pleaded with the attorney.

"I'm just telling you the reality of the situation, and I suggest this to be the route you take."

We motioned for Frances to join us and explained the situation to her. She cried and told me she just wanted William to be at home with her. "He's too old to go to jail," she cried.

We debated the pros and cons of pleading not guilty until court went into session. I took a seat beside Frances, who took my hand and squeezed it tightly. All too soon the charges against William were read. He took his seat beside the judge, his medal still under his arm.

The matter was settled in less than five minutes. As the district attorney read the charge of child molestation, people seated around us laughed at the old man and immediately pronounced their own judgment. Frances squeezed my hand even tighter and shut her eyes. William appeared small and defenseless in front of the court. The judge peered over the documents he was signing and asked William how he wished to plead, but the attorney answered for him. Several minutes of hushed conversation occurred between the judge, the district attorney, and the counselor. In no time at all, it was over.

When the judge instructed him to step down, William looked at him and announced in a proud, firm voice: "I am not guilty."

With tired sympathetic eyes, the judge stated that he understood the plea and William could step down. He held his medals for the judge to see, but the judge was signing the paperwork documenting the case.

Before he was released to go home with Frances, William was forced to spend the better part of the day in jail. He was even transported to the county prison, experienced the humiliation of a strip search, given a prisoner's uniform, and locked in a cell with several others. At five o'clock, he was abruptly pulled from the dinner table and released to his trembling wife.

He learned that the most lenient possible sentence had been bestowed, and the prison experience was simply a ploy to drive home the seriousness of the charge. He would be on probation for the next four years and required to attend counseling. He would not be allowed to spend time alone with anyone under fourteen years of age. If nothing happened during the four years, his record would be wiped clean. Frances said that if they were younger, they would have pleaded not guilty.

In spite of Jordy's absolution from sin, it was still some time before William returned to The Breakfast Club on a regular basis. Tybee residents had become equally divided in their condemnation or support of William. His case had been the primary topic of discussion for weeks on the island and, even though William continued to profess his innocence, friends of the Jones family persisted in their damnation.

We missed William during the morning shift. We continued to laugh and cut up with one another, but without William the sense of loss was sometimes oppressive. The gossip eventually died, although our feelings for William and Frances did not. Those who loved him visited the house and encouraged him to get on with his life. Frances resolved to stick beside William whenever he left the house, lest he find himself in a confrontational situation without a witness.

The matter ended as suddenly as it had begun. While we were seated at the counter one morning, reading our newspapers and drinking our coffee, William entered the restaurant. Appearing timid and uncertain, he mumbled greetings that were a shadow of his normal behavior. Everyone immediately stopped what they were doing and gleefully pumped his hand. His coffee cup was filled, and the fellowship welcomed back the self-imposed prodigal son.

Over the next several weeks, people continued to argue William's guilt and innocence. He would carefully recount his version of the charges whenever people asked him what had happened. On numerous mornings, the congregation of The Breakfast Club would relive the charge, trial, and outcome as William took the time to explain the situation to anyone who asked—and many people asked.

As time passes, however, other topics have crept into the conversation, placing William's life on a back burner. Jordy has purchased season tickets for the Jacksonville Jaguars football team. Wilson explains how life is lived in Cleveland. Johnny expounds on Rush Limbaugh. Bill discusses who will win the World Series.

Now, things are as different as they are the same. Barry is married and goes to the mall as much as he goes fishing. Bill continues to train for his sports call-in show. Jordy still does a thousand things at once. Most recently, he has concentrated on building a half-court basketball area in his driveway. Jean is back after traveling to some corner of the world and is already planning her next trip. Daniel and Jenny's daughter is home and healing from the accident; Daniel has resumed his shark fishing.

The morning shift meets every morning and dispenses and receives grace and support so that everyone can make it through another day. I believe no matter how bad a particular day may prove to be, The Church of The Breakfast Club will be there to sustain us through the trials and tribulations of life. It is the type of church God would be most comfortable in, and I am certain he visits often.

Notes

[1] *Won't You Come Billy Bob Bailey* (Atlanta: Peachtree Publishers, Ltd., 1980) 8.

[2] Bob Verdi, *Holy Cow* (New York: Villard Books, 1989) 207.

When the Moon Came down Tenth Street

I t is dusk on this April Monday. The moon is so large and bright as it rises that it gives the impression it is walking up the crosswalk and will proceed right down Tenth Street, past our house and across the island to the marshes. Today is also my daughter's fourteenth birthday. She and her friends have finished eating the hamburgers I cooked, the cake has been consumed, and they are down the street on the beach. Because they are wearing their bathing suits, Janice is afraid they are in the water. The last thing she wants is to explain to parents why their daughters went swimming. Besides, she is tired and doesn't want to be bothered with washing a load of towels after we finish cleaning up the kitchen. She has dispatched me to collect the girls before their parents begin arriving, but I am mesmerized by the moon on the crosswalk and the sound of waves kissing the shore.

Jeremy breaks the spell by yelling out the score of the baseball game he is watching. I nod at the window, thanking him for the information, and look down the street. Given a choice between television sports and the beauty of nature, Jeremy will always choose the former. On the other hand, I enjoy looking at stars and typically take a brief stroll around the deck before going to bed.

This time of year is quiet. Tourists come only on weekends, and islanders are home finishing their suppers and—if they are lucky—sitting on their decks watching the orange-yellow moon climb above the sea. The summer residents of the street are also gone, returning to Savannah earlier in the evening. The lights are dim. No snippets of conversation are to be detected. I recall last night's gathering of Tenth Street residents, the first of the season, where everyone turned out to discuss past Fourth of July parades and to begin planning this year's extravaganza. Someone claimed the permit had already been taken care of so we wouldn't have to worry about the police. The moon continues to rise, losing the orange and turning glaring white.

Running with the Dolphins and Other Tybee Tales

As I backed the car out of the driveway this morning for my daily trek to The Breakfast Club, I watched the sun rise. It popped out of the ocean, chasing the night away. It was clear and bright, the sky was already blue, and I had to stop in the middle of the road and look. A few stars lingered, captivated by the morning glow and not wanting to remain with the night. On the other side of the sky, the moon had also refused to leave, fading away but not retreating from its position. Even before my first cup of coffee, I knew there were few others in the world today sharing the sight. Now things are in reverse, having come full circle, and the sun is retreating while the moon is commanding the tides and my undivided attention.

Janice must have noticed me from the kitchen window because Chelsea, our five-year-old, rushes down with a flashlight in her hand. She offers her services as my guide and, taking my hand, leads me down the street. Kristen and her best friend Melissa top the crosswalk, celebrating the ecstasy of youth with the full moon over their shoulders. The rest of her friends catch up when she pauses to kiss me and thank me for cooking the hamburgers. I watch her walk away, knowing full well that her time with me is beginning to end. All too soon, Janice and I will live here alone.

Chelsea pulls me along, asking if we can swing. Last year the city decided that old-fashioned swings on the beach would be a nice touch and had them built at the end of most streets. Chelsea keeps the light focused straight ahead as we cross the Valley of the Sea Chicken. Between the second and third dune, we sit in the swing. The moon's trail on the water looks like a sidewalk leading to the Gulf Stream. There is no phosphorus in the water yet, bringing its own reflection of the moon on top of the waves, but in a few weeks it will seem the moon is underwater as well. The dark outline of a dog rushes by the ocean's end, followed by a young man's shadow. Chelsea asks if it is her brother, and I tell her no.

Janice appears from the dunes, sits beside me, and lays her tired head on my shoulder. The atmosphere is peaceful, and the only sound is the waves. Channel markers blink on and off on the horizon. Chelsea runs across the dunes into the darkness but turns the flashlight on, and we can see where she is. In a few minutes we will return home, walking in silence, hand in hand, down the street where our house sits. The ocean will continue to sing throughout the night, and we'll hear its song through open windows. It will be a good night's sleep, and, should we wake, the waves will sing us back into a peaceful slumber. Tomorrow, the sun and moon will cause me to stop in the middle of the road again, reminding me that this is home.